PRINCIPLES AND PRACTICES OF ENGINEERING AND INDUSTRIAL ECONOMICS

ENGINEERING TOOLS, TECHNIQUES AND TABLES

Additional books in this series can be found on Nova's website under the Series tab.

Additional e-books in this series can be found on Nova's website under the e-book tab.

ECONOMIC ISSUES, PROBLEMS AND PERSPECTIVES

Additional books in this series can be found on Nova's website under the Series tab.

Additional e-books in this series can be found on Nova's website under the e-book tab.

ENGINEERING TOOLS, TECHNIQUES AND TABLES

PRINCIPLES AND PRACTICES OF ENGINEERING AND INDUSTRIAL ECONOMICS

M. HOSSAIN ALI

nova publishers

New York

Library of Congress Cataloging-in-Publication Data

Principles and practices of engineering and industrial economics / editor, M. Hossain Ali, Faculty of Civil Engineering and Earth Resources, University Malaysia Pahang, and others.
      pages cm
  Includes index.
  ISBN 978-1-62417-596-1 (hardcover)
  1. Engineering economy. 2. Industrial organization (Economic theory) I. Ali, M. Hossain, editor of compilation.
  TA177.4.P75 2013
  338.5--dc23
                                          2012047140

Published by Nova Science Publishers, Inc. † *New York*

CONTENTS

Preface   vii

Chapter 1   **Concept, Need, and Role of Engineering Economics**   **1**

1.1. Introduction: Background and General Perspectives   *1*

1.2. Economic Perspectives on Engineering Technology and Project   *2*

1.3. Concept of Engineering Economics   *2*

1.4. Steps in Decision Making Process   *3*

1.5. Significance of Economic Analysis of Engineering Works/Projects   *5*

1.6. Role of Economic Analysis in Decision Making Process   *6*

Chapter 2   **Fundamentals and Applications of Economic Theories**   **9**

2.1. Concept of Economics and Finance   *9*

2.2. Demand and Supply   *10*

2.3. Cost and Revenue   *13*

2.4. Cost Estimation – Importance, Components, and Relevant Factors   *16*

2.5. Economic Production Strategy Identification:
Methods and Applications   *21*

2.6. Economic Decision Tools – Cost Analysis   *29*

2.7. Profitability analysis   *36*

2.8. Price Indices   *40*

2.9. Factors Affecting Value of Money   *42*

2.10. Tax Calculation for Income   *44*

2.11. Valuation of Assets - Salvage Value, Economic Life, Depreciation,
Depletion   *45*

2.12. Some Relevant Economic Terminologies   *50*

2.13. Workout Problems   *52*

Chapter 3   **Data Sources, Demand Forecasting, and Cost Estimation for Project Analysis**   **69**

3.1. Types of Data Required   *69*

3.2. Demand Forecasting and Determination of Design Capacity   *70*

3.3. Data Sources   *74*

3.4. Cost Estimation   *76*

References   *97*

Chapter 4   **Fundamentals and Theories of Financial Analysis for Project**
                  Evaluation   **99**
                  4.1. Background   *99*
                  4.2. Financial Analysis   *99*
                  4.3. Different Financial Indices and Related Terminologies *101*
                  4.4. Expression of Cost and Benefit   *105*
                  4.5. Analysis of Net Present Value (NPV)   *107*
                  4.6. The NPV Curve   *109*
                  4.7. Discounting/Compounding Formula under Different Perspectives *110*
                  4.8. Other Factors to Be Considered in Financial Statement *113*
                  4.9. Application of Compounding Formula for Interest Calculation *113*
                  4.10. Workout Problems   *114*

Chapter 5   **Indicators and Decision Rules for Project Selection**
                  among Alternatives   **123**
                  5.1. Indicators for Project Judgment   *123*
                  5.2. Determination of the Indicators   *124*
                  5.3. Selection Criteria   *125*
                  5.4. Other Considerations for "Governmental (Public)" and "Private"
                  *   Investment/ Project*   *126*
                  5.5. Workout Problems   *127*

Chapter 6   **Risks and Uncertainties in Engineering Projects**   **143**
                  6.1. Background and Perspectives   *143*
                  6.2. Uncertainties   *143*
                  6.3. Sensitivity Analysis   *144*
                  6.4. Risk   *145*
                  6.5. Uncertainties, Risks, and Their Management in Water Resources
                  *   Sector*   *151*
                  6.6. Environmental Screening   *153*
                  6.7. Final Selection of Project   *155*

Chapter 7   **Time for Equipment Replacement**   **157**
                  7.1. Background   *157*
                  7.2. The Need for a Replacement Study   *157*
                  7.3. Factors Affecting Replacement   *159*
                  7.4. Replacement Method/Procedure   *165*
                  7.5. Workout Problem   *169*
                  References   *171*

Chapter 8   **Models and Softwares in Economic and Financial Analysis** **173**
                  8.1. Basics of Model: General Concepts   *173*
                  8.2. Economic Model   *173*
                  8.3. Softwares /Tools for Financial Analysis   *180*
                  References   *182*

Index   **183**

PREFACE

Economic analysis is the monetary evaluation of alternatives for meeting a given objective. An engineering economic study involves technical considerations and it is a comparison between technical alternatives in which the differences between the alternatives are expressed so far as practicable in monetary terms. The engineering economic analysts test the profitability of a proposed operation, or choose the best option among the existing alternatives. These calculations are such a necessary part of the numerous choices between technical alternatives that every engineer has to do as a part of his design function or process.

Different economic analytical techniques such as Cost-benefit and Cost-effectiveness analyses are used by various clients in many domains, including various development projects (energy, environment, water development projects, transportation), prioritizing industrial projects, comparison of building projects, evaluation of energy and water conservation measures, and in the field of climate change, homeland security, workforce, etc. The design engineer use 'Economic Analysis' to evaluate design alternatives. Building owners use of economic analysis to determine the most economically efficient or cost-effective choice among building alternatives. If an executive disregards the economic effects of a decision, he is disregarding the cost commitments that will result from his decision. This book "Principles and Practices of Engineering & Industrial Economics" covers issues ranging from project formulation steps - through data collection, costing of project, detail financial analysis, decision rules, risk analysis and environmental considerations – to model study for financial & scenario analysis for decision making. In the formulation of text, it is assumed that the readers have no background knowledge of Economics. Preliminary knowledge in Economics is helpful, but not essential.

Chapter 1: This chapter discusses background, importance, and issues relevant to economic analysis of projects & engineering works. Economic consideration is essential in all sorts of decision making. In order to satisfy the goal of maximizing benefits (which may be of monetary, environmental, or social) per dollar expended, economic principles and techniques should be used at all levels of the activities - planning, program implementation, and program evaluation at the field, state, regional and national level. Economic analysis provides a systematic approach for studying the allocation of resources to achieve an organization's objectives. Businesses, government agencies and nonprofit organizations use economic analysis techniques for a variety of purposes. It helps ensure cost-effective operations, minimize overhead, and compare costs to expected benefits.

Chapter 2: Before going to financial analysis of engineering & industrial projects, knowledge of fundamental aspects and theories of economics is essential. There are many economic concepts, theories, and principles which should be taken into account in engineering studies. This chapter focusses and discusses on these aspects. Methods of economic analysis help ensure cost-effective operations, minimize overhead and compare costs to expected benefits. Economics can help investors understand the potential ramifications of national policy and events on business conditions. Understanding economics can also give investors the tools to predict macroeconomic conditions and understand the implications of those predictions on companies, stocks, markets and so on. Being able to project/forecast that a certain set of government policies will stoke (or choke off) inflation or growth in a country can certainly help stock and bond investors position themselves appropriately.

Chapter 3: Proper preparation of an economic analysis requires a major effort to gather data, do mathematical calculations, and summarize results into required report formats. Accurately forecasting the cost and outcome/benefit of future projects is vital for its success. The first step in financial and economic analysis of engineering development project is to identify appropriate data and to understand their potential and their limitations. This chapter provides an overview of the data needs for economic analysis, considering how data requirements may vary depending on the analytical issues at hand. The chapter also provides a brief guide to different sources of data and their respective limitations, and detail cost analyses for the proposed project.

Chapter 4: The purpose of economic analysis of engineering (and also for other) projects is to increase the net output measured at economic prices in the national economy. An investment or intervention is said to be economically efficient when it maximizes the value of output from the resources available. In economic and financial decision making, we need several types of evaluation and detail analysis of financial aspects. This chapter elaborated the financial analysis protocols.

Chapter 5: We are interested in such a project that will yield a greater output for national economy. A test of economic viability needs to be applied for single project as well as multiple options. Different indicators (such as NPV, IRR, BCR) are used to compare the project alternatives. There are comparative merits and demerits of the indicators. This chapter discusses the relative merits & demerits of the indicators, their determination procedures, decision rules for selecting projects among multiple alternatives, and sample illustrations for selecting projects based on the criterions.

Chapter 6: In evaluating capital budgeting decisions, quantitative approaches are useful when there are lower levels of uncertainty. When uncertainty increases and forecasting becomes difficult, the value of quantitative approaches decreases. Engineers, executives, and managers need to address the critical nature of risk and uncertainty in the decision-making process. Identification of the risks and uncertainties inherent in a proposed action, assessment of their impact on the possible outcomes, and design of contingency plans to manage them are essential for making sound project/business decisions. Without completing these activities, decisions made and undertaken are likely to be sub-optimal ones, leading to organizations being less competitive in the marketplace. This chapter focuses on the qualitative aspects of projects relating to risks and uncertainties, and strategic measures to reduce risks and uncertainties under the prevailing conditions.

Chapter 7: The performance of almost everything declines with age. The Equipment replacement system is one of the industrial problems for management. A large amount of annual capital investment needs correct information for proper allocation and utilization. The replacement timing, selection, and method used for reaching decisions are some of the important factors in the efficient operation and utilization of the resource. Replacement decisions (to decide whether we should keep an existing unit of equipment or replace it with a new unit) are more important in market oriented economy where competition of the market is bringing profit margins to be minimal. This chapter illustrates the equipment replacement issues and procedures.

Chapter 8: Almost all managerial decisions are based on forecasts. Every decision becomes operational at some point in the future, so it should be based on forecasts of future conditions. Forecasts are needed continually, and as time moves on, the impact of the forecasts on actual performance is measured; original forecasts are updated; and decisions are modified, and so on. The decision-maker uses forecasting models to assist him or her in decision-making process. The purpose of models is to aid in designing solutions. They are to assist understanding the problem and to aid deliberation and choice by allowing us to evaluate the consequence of our action before implementing them. This chapter overviews the *Economic models* and *Tolls for Financial Analysis* for alternative policy analysis.

M. Hossain Ali
Agricultural Engineering Division
Bangladesh Institute of Nuclear Agriculture
BAU Campus, Mymensingh, Bangladesh
www.mhali.com
Formar Visiting Senior Lecturer
School of Civil Engineering & Earth Resources
University Malaysia Pahang

Chapter 1

CONCEPT, NEED, AND ROLE
OF ENGINEERING ECONOMICS

1.1. INTRODUCTION:
BACKGROUND AND GENERAL PERSPECTIVES

In general, everyone has to make important life decisions about work - deciding, for example, whether to take a job for the first time, or leave the workforce to care for children, go to school, or retire. Every day, millions of peoples are making economic decisions. Consumers are choosing among a vast array of goods and services and deciding how much income they want to save and where they want to invest it. The firms are making decisions about hiring workers, about investing in new projects, plants, equipment, and technology, and about what and how much to produce. Government policies, tax system, interest rates, and inflation can influence all of those decisions. Higher marginal tax rates can reduce work effort, discourage saving, and slow the growth of the economy. Changes in entitlement programs for the elderly can influence people's decisions about retirement and saving for the future. Reducing the budget deficit can boost the national capital stock, lower interest rates, and raise gross domestic product. Increased regulation and governmental mandates can reduce productivity. In addition, world events can also affect a nation's economy. An economic storm in Asia can roll across the Pacific, or vice versa.

Economic consideration is essential in all sorts of decision making. In order to satisfy the goal of maximizing benefits (which may be of monetary, environmental, or social) per dollar expended, economic principles and techniques should be used at all levels of the activities - planning, program implementation, and program evaluation at the field, state, regional and national level. It provides cost effective assistance to customers, cooperators, and partners for the sustained use of resources. It is equally applicable to personal, family, or society levels.

Economic analysis provides a systematic approach for studying the allocation of resources to achieve an organization's objectives. Techniques of economic analysis help ensure efficient operations, minimize overhead and compare costs and benefits. Businesses, government agencies and nonprofit organizations use economic analysis techniques for a variety of purposes. Tools of economic analysis are especially popular in the medical and pharmaceutical industries, which use these methods to assess the costs and effects of new medications and medical therapies. Methods of economic analysis help ensure cost-effective operations, minimize overhead cost and compare costs to expected benefits.

Economic principles and techniques include cost effectiveness, economic feasibility, partial budgeting, and profitability analysis (benefit-cost ratio, net present benefit). Appropriate analyses should be performed for problem solving options.

1.2. ECONOMIC PERSPECTIVES ON ENGINEERING TECHNOLOGY AND PROJECT

In engineering, and broadly applicable to any field, a '*technology*' must offer a high financial rate of return. An investment or intervention is said to be economically efficient when it maximizes the value of output from the resources available.

Economic analysis is helpful in identifying opportunities to increase the net values generated with limited resources by various techniques/alternatives, and in designing policies that encourage stakeholders and agency personnel to improve resource management practices in ways that enhance social net benefits.

Every entity, whether public or private, is confronted with the economic problem. Economic analysis provides a systematic approach to answering the economic questions. The Engineers, like other professionals, is confronted by the basic economic problem of scarcity. Resource and budgetary limitations make it impossible to undertake all actions which are deemed desirable, thus necessitating choices among alternative uses of resources and funds. An economic analysis helps to determine which, among various alternatives, is the economically best course of action for achieving a given objective.

In many practical problems, we, the engineers, face multiple alternatives in selecting a development plan or project.

In such situation, we have to decide the right thing (the best one) – the technology, the structure, project adoption and implementation, etc. among alternatives.

Economic merit of a project is judged by comparing projected benefits with projected costs. Under normal condition, an engineering development project should be technically feasible, economically viable, socially acceptable, and environmentally sustainable. So, we have to consider technical performance, durability, financial involvement (input), outcome/output, environmental aspects, etc.

Economic analysis of income and services producing from investment is thus essential. In engineering activities, or activities having a major role of engineers, the engineers are best fitted to analyze such thing due to their background in engineering principles.

1.3. CONCEPT OF ENGINEERING ECONOMICS

Engineers are involved in planning, designing, implementing, and operating the development work/project. For individuals, public sector (Govt.) projects, or private corporations; either for development works or business farms, our objective is to maximize output (return) from the available (or investable) resource. For that, the manager, engineer, or corporate president has to decide whether the proposed work/project/technology is economically viable and should be materialized, or to choose a project from alternatives.

Engineering economics deals with mathematical techniques that justify economic viability of an engineering work/project, or perform economic comparison among alternatives.

It involves formulating, analyzing, and comparing economic outcomes of defined engineering work(s)/project(s). The comparison is performed based on a set of criterion.

Many examples of engineering activities can be given. Engineering activities/projects are undertaken to solve a problem. For example – water supply problem, traffic load problem, housing problem (constructing single-story or multi-story building), etc. As a simple example, let's consider that we want to make a table – it may be wooden, steel, wooden top with steel frame, glass/ceramic top with wooden frame, etc. How we can judge the alternatives?

To do this, we should know the answer of the following questions:

1. How much each item will cost? (initial investment)
2. Is there any maintenance cost ? (maintenance/operating cost)
3. What is the effective life for each option? (outcome)
4. What is the basis for selecting one from the alternatives? (rule/criteria)

1.4. STEPS IN DECISION MAKING PROCESS

For the best possible outcome from a project, a systematic and well documented process should be followed. For evaluating multiple options, the same financial analytical procedure should be followed for each case. The steps in decision making process can be summarized as follows:

(i)   Realize the problem (problem statement) and define the objective(s)
(ii) Formulate possible (realistic) solution options
(iii) Collect relevant data (for each option)
(iv) Estimate/analyze cost and benefit (in an unified, suitable format)
(v)   Evaluate the 'economic outcome' (net total benefit) using economic criterion, and decide:

     a) Whether the project (in case of single project) is economically viable or not, or
     b) Prioritize the options (in terms of maximum net benefit) from the alternatives (in case of multiple options), and categorize them according to decreasing net benefit

(vi) Considering other factors along with economic indicators, take final decision on:

     a) Acceptance of the project, or rejection (for a single project option)
     b) Select the best one from the alternatives (for multiple options)

No.(iv) involves a bit mathematics, No.(v) involves some 'criteria'/ 'decision rule', and analyzing the indicator values.

i) Realize the Problem (Problem Statement) and Define the Objective(s)

Engineering projects are initiated to solve a problem. In order to solve a problem, the problem characteristics must be clearly understood and identified (e.g. cause and effect relationship, and/or source-sink relations), along with the characteristics of its desired solution. Correct definition of the problem and setting problem-solving objective are the good start of the project.

ii) Formulate Possible (Realistic) Solution Options

Once the problem has been defined and the objective has been formulated, all possible solution alternatives must be identified and documented. The solution options should be such that it is technically feasible, environmentally sound, and financially feasible and cost-effective. In finding solution options, the engineers should employ/devote his creativity based on his theoretical knowledge and practical experiences. Appropriate and talent solution option can make the project simple, less money and time consuming. As the resources available to analyze the alternatives are limited, we must produce a reasonable set of alternatives. This requires engineering judgment to identify which proposals are likely to fail and make sure that they are eliminated early, so as not to waste the limited resources for analyzing them.

iii) Collect Relevant Data (For Each Option)

For all feasible solution options, the engineers must analyze in detail for final scrutiny of the option. For this purpose, various types of information/data may be required – technical, demand and supply, financial, managerial, etc. Accurate and valid data of required type can only produce accurate output/result. So, proper care should be undertaken and appropriate methodology should be followed.

iv) Estimate/Analyze Cost and Benefit (In an Unified, Suitable Format)

After collecting the required data, analyze the total cost involvement and total benefit from each option. The qualitative benefits and costs should be converted to quantitative/monetary form with acceptable conversion rate, and should be similar for all options. Finally, summary of the costs and benefits should be documented.

v) Evaluate the 'Economic Outcome' Using Economic Criterion, and Formulate Economic Prioritization

The associated costs and benefits (outcomes from the project) should be judged based on the appropriate economic indicators and criterion, and a priority list should be made. Then, comment on the acceptance or rejection can be made for single option.

vi) Considering Other Factors Along with Economic Indicators, Take Final Decision

Economic outcome is not the only target or criteria in selecting a project. Other relevant factors (discussed in a later section) should be considered along with the economic criterion, and a final decision should be taken based on the priority factor.

Engineers are appropriate for doing financial analysis and economic decision making process for engineering works/projects, as they know in-and-out of the engineering works; subject to they are well trained in engineering economics.

1.5. SIGNIFICANCE OF ECONOMIC ANALYSIS OF ENGINEERING WORKS/PROJECTS

Significance of economic analysis of engineering works is hidden within the definition of "*engineering*" itself. In a generous word, 'engineering' is the art of utilizing natural resources for the benefit of mankind. The word 'benefit' demands for 'maximizing the benefit'; which could be obtained by comparing economic outcome (net financial benefit) among possible alternative uses of the materials/resources. Some examples of engineering works are:

Problem	Solution options	Engineering works/options
(1) Water crisis (have to satisfy the demand by increasing supply)	- surface water storage	Construction of dam: - earthen - concrete/RCC - rubber dam
	- diversion channel/ artificial river	Construction of artificial channel/river: - earthen - concrete
	- groundwater abstraction	Installation of tube-well / Establishment of well-field
	- purification of polluted/ contaminated water	Set up of water purification plant
	- artificial rain	Performing works (steps) for cloud seeding/artificial rain
	- import of freshwater from nearby country	Construction of pipe line
(2) Electricity crisis (have to satisfy the demand by increasing generation)	- Hydro-electric power plant	Construction of dam and set up of hydro-electric power plant
	- Thermal power plant	Set up of thermal power plant: - From coal - From diesel/patrol - From gas
	- Nuclear power plant	Set up of nuclear power plant
	- Renewable energy (solar, wind, wave, geo-thermal) use	Set up of renewable energy farm: - Wind - Solar - Wave - Geo-thermal

(Continued)

Problem	Solution options	Engineering works/options
(3) Residence crisis in the town (to meet the residential demand)	- Single-story building	Construction of single-story building
	- High-rise (multi-story) building	Construction of high-rise building (along with other facility – playground, shop, mosque, etc.)
(4) Transport/traffic load problem (to decrease the traffic jam)	- Fly-over - Diversion network - Tram /road rail - Underground rail	Construction of the same.

As the resources are becoming scarce and have alternative uses, evaluation of different alternatives is pre-requisite to achieve economic efficiency. Economic efficiency is achieved when limited resources are used in a manner that generates the greatest net value. Economic analysis can be helpful in identifying inefficient allocation of resources, and in determining strategies for moving towards an efficient allocation. Economic analysis is an essential part of decision making process. The role of economic analysis can be viewed in money cycle (Figure 1.1).

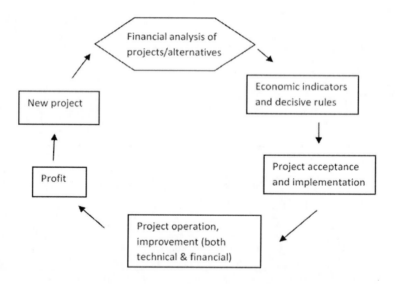

Figure 1.1. Typical Money cycle with reference to engineering project.

1.6. ROLE OF ECONOMIC ANALYSIS IN DECISION MAKING PROCESS

1.6.1. Typical Criteria of a Technology

In engineering works, and broadly applicable to any field, a 'technology' should have the following criteria:

a) *The technology must offer a high financial rate of return.*
A possible increase of 10 to 20 percent in yield/output will not stimulate rapid uptake. This requires a return of 40 – 100 percent or more.

b) *The technology must offer a quick payoff.*
For crops (agricultural sector) this should be in terms of half-year or less. Forestry projects require longer but the recommendation is " if you want to get trees planted, go for quick-growing species not slow-growing one".

c) *A new technology must involve low risk, preferably reducing the existing risk.*

d) *The technology must have low inputs.*
For the farmer, the technology should require low cash and low inputs of labour. For the government, the technology should avoid recurrent costs, it should have a low import content and maximum use of locally available materials. It should avoid maintenance which requires imported spares or high levels of skill.

e) *The technology should be easy to teach and demonstrate*
For widespread adoption there must be the multiplier effect of farmers (or producers) teaching other farmers (or producers). A project which requires large inputs of engineers or of imported machinery, will inevitably be restricted to small project areas. A technology which requires a saturation level of extension agents/personnels, will be restricted to a short period of time or a limited area.

f) *The technology should be socially acceptable*
Success of a technology depends on the positive and quick response of the users, willingness to accept it.

g) *The technology should be environment-friendly*
The technology should not dispose of hazardous materials that are harmful to environment.

1.6.2. Factors Affecting Decision Making Process

The factors affecting decision making process of a project involve:

1. Total net financial return
2. Rate of financial return
3. Financial involvement / Initial capital investment
4. Operating cost
5. Maintenance cost
6. Involvement of foreign currency / input / expertise
7. National/State/Province priority
8. Employment generation
9. Nature of technology (high/medium/low) *or* labour (intensive/non-intensive) involvement
10. Risk / uncertainty associated with the project
11. Future well-being / Future development prospect
12. Environmental aspects / environmental sustainability
13. Social acceptance

1.6.3. Role of Economic Criteria in Decision Making Process

The economic criterion is not the only decisive criteria in decision making process. Although the objective of most projects is to maximize the net financial return, it is not the unique criteria. Other factors (described earlier) should also be considered. The importance/weight of other factors depends on the impact of the project on the particular factor, and national priority. Then, applying judgment, the optimal one (project) should be selected which minimizes adverse/bad effects and maximizes overall social benefits.

1.6.4. Impact of Economic Decision in Engineering Projects on Social, National, and Global Context

Engineering works/projects are designed to meet society's/regional/ national need. If for a society, a certain amount of budget is allocated for development work, and the planner fails to choose the best project which maximizes net return, the society will be deprived from financial benefit. Similarly, for regional and national level projects, the society and the nation will be deprived from the benefit.

In global context, project should be undertaken where it is more economically viable. For example, if it is planned to produce rice in Saudi Arabia or Iraq where water is scarce, it will not be a wise decision; rather more rice can be produced in Asian countries (with some measures) where rainfall or water is abundant. Similarly, it will be wise to produce electricity from solar energy at Sahara and Australia where the sunshine is abundant, than the Asian countries. Thus, the people at global scale will be more benefited. Of course, this calls for strengthening of global trade.

Exercise
(1.1)   Define 'Engineering Economics'. Describe the importance of economic analysis in engineering works.
(1.2)   What is the subject matter of 'Engineering Economics'? Do you think that economic analysis of engineering works/projects is essential?
(1.3)   Discuss the ideal criteria of an engineering technology.
(1.4)   Describe the factors affecting decision making process in engineering projects.
(1.5)   Do you think that economic criterion is the major selection criteria of Engineering project? Discuss.
(1.6)   What is the role of economic criteria in decision making process?
(1.7)   Narrate the steps to be followed in decision making process of an engineering project.
(1.8)   Identify 10 Engineering works (including the problem on which it is based) and their alternatives.
(1.9)   Describe the money cycle (with reference to engineering project) with a sketch.
(1.10) Discuss the impact of economic decision in engineering project on social, national, and global context.

Chapter 2

FUNDAMENTALS AND APPLICATIONS OF ECONOMIC THEORIES

There are many economic concepts, theories, and principles which should be taken into account in engineering studies. In principle, economics deals with the interactions between men and wealth; while engineering is concerned with maximizing the benefit from the wealth *or* natural resources, or find cost-effective ways to achieve a target. Economic principles are applied in engineering design optimization. Thus, the objectives of economics and engineering works are almost similar and linked.

Economics can help investors understand the potential ramifications of national policy and events on business conditions. Understanding economics can also give investors the tools to predict macroeconomic conditions and understand the implications of those predictions on companies, stocks, markets and so on. Being able to project/forcast that a certain set of government policies will stoke (or choke off) inflation or growth in a country, can certainly help stock and bond investors position themselves appropriately.

2.1. CONCEPT OF ECONOMICS AND FINANCE

2.1.1. Economy and Economics

'Economy' is the condition of wealth, goods and services whereas 'Economics' is the subject which deals with economy. The economy encompasses everything related to the production and consumption of goods and services in an area. It includes large set of inter-related economic production and consumption activities which aid in determining how scarce resources are allocated.

The economy and the factors affecting the economy have spawned one of the largest fields of study in human history - economics. It is concerned with money flows, trade activities, and industrial systems in the society. In essence, economics is a social science which examines people's behaviour with wealth/resource according to their self-interests. Economists use the scientific approach for developing economic theories. Economics studies how individuals, governments, firms and nations make choices on allocating scarce resources to satisfy their unlimited wants. The study of economics can be broken down into two major areas of focus: microeconomics and macroeconomics. Macroeconomics concentrates on the behaviour of the aggregate economy, and microeconomics focuses on individual consumers.

The economists try to understand how consumers and producers react to changing conditions. Economics can provide powerful guidance and influence to policy-making at the national level. There are very real consequences to how a nation approaches taxation, regulation, and government spending; economics can offer advice and analysis regarding these decisions.

2.1.2. Economics and Finance

Finance is the science that describes the management of money, banking, credit, investments, and assets. Basically, finance looks at anything that has to do with money and the market.

Finance generally focuses on the study of prices, interest rates, money flows and the financial markets. Thinking more broadly, finance seems to be most concerned with notions like the time value of money, rates of return, cost of capital, optimal financial structures and the quantification of risk.

'Economics' and 'Finance' are interrelated, and inform & influence each other. Investors care about these studies because they also influence the markets to a great degree.

Because all of our resources are limited in comparison to all of our wants and needs, individuals and nations have to make decisions regarding what goods and services they can buy and which ones they must forgo. So, because of scarcity, people and economist must make decisions over how to allocate their resources. Economics, in turn, aims to study why we make these decisions and how we allocate our resources most efficiently.

2.2. DEMAND AND SUPPLY

2.2.1. Concepts, Characteristics, and Behavior of Demand and Supply Curve

The market price of an item is determined by both supply and demand of that item. *Demand* represents how much (quantity) of an item (product or service) is desired by buyers. *Supply* represents how much the market can offer. *The quantity demanded* is the amount of an item people are willing to buy at a certain price. *The quantity supplied* refers to the amount of a certain item the growers are willing to supply in exchange of a certain price.

Graphical presentation of quantity demanded of a good versus price is termed as *demand curve* (Figure 2.1). The demand curve indicates negative relationship between price and quantity. *The law of demand* states that, if all other factors remain unchanged, the higher the price of a good, the less will be the demand for that good. Because, to buy that good, the people have to avoid consumption of other goods which they may have value more.

Graphical presentation of quantity supplied of a good versus price is termed as *supply curve* (Figure 2.2). The supply curve shows an upward slope, meaning that the higher the price, the higher the quantity supplied. The law of supply states that, if all other factors remain unchanged, the higher the price of a good, the higher will be the supply of that good.

This happens because at a higher price, the producer will earn more revenue by selling higher quantity.

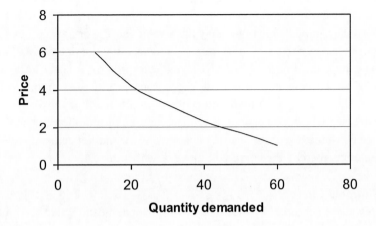

Figure 2.1. Schematic of a demand curve.

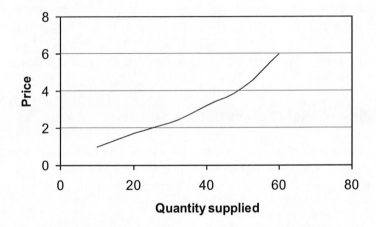

Figure 2.2. Schematic of a supply curve.

Therefore, price is a reflection of supply and demand. The relationship between demand and supply underlies the forces behind the allocation of resources. Under perfect market economy condition, the demand and supply theory will allocate resources in the most efficient way possible.

2.2.2. Why the 'Demand Curve' Moves Downward and 'Supply Curve' Moves Upward

The law of demand and supply are based on the assumption that, the market is not monopoly (i.e. not controlled only by suppler or buyer) and all other factors remain unchanged. That is, the population of the region, the income of the people, test of goods, supply and price of other alternative items, etc. are constant.

The Case of Demand Curve

The relationship between 'price' and 'quantity demanded' is negative (Figure 2.1). That is, with the increase in price, the demand decreases, thus the curve moves downward. This is because, if the price of a good increases, to buy that good, the people have to avoid consumption of other goods which they may have value more – or have to buy less amount of that item, to balance with the income (as the income did not increase). For example, a consumer has a fixed income of 1000 $/year, and the price of a specific item, say 'cloth', increased by 30%. To balance the budget, the consumer has two options – to reduce the consumption of the 'cloth', or to avoid other items to allocate budget for the 'cloth'. If the other items are essential (that is, cannot be reduced in use/consumption), the only other option is to reduce the consumption of the 'cloth'. That's why, the market demand will decrease with the increase in price, thereby the curve will move downward.

The Case of Supply Curve

The supply curve (Figure 2.2) shows an upward slope, meaning that the higher the price, the higher the quantity supplied. This happens because at a higher price, the producer/supplier will earn more revenue by selling higher quantity. For example, price of 'rice' is low in the market. As a producer, you will stock the rice for future possible increase in price, or will grow/cultivate fewer amounts; thus as a whole the supply in the market will be decreased. When the price will increase, you will sell the stock (or will grow more). That means, supply in the market will be increased. That's why the direction of the curve is upward.

2.2.3. Equilibrium Point (At Demand and Supply)

According to the principles of economics, the price level of an item is determined by the point at which quantity supplied equals quantity demanded. To illustrate this, consider the case in which the supply and demand curves are plotted on the same graph (Figure 2.3).

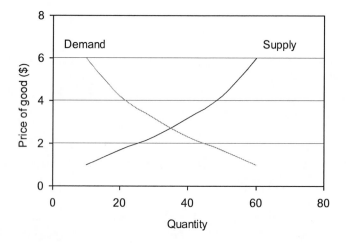

Figure 2.3. Intersection of supply and demand curve.

In the figure, the price of the good corresponds to that point where the supply and demand curves cross. This point is termed as equilibrium point. An economy is assumed to be an equilibrium system in which various quantities affect other through competitive market mechanisms. Economic properties are the effect of large numbers of rational consumers and producers interacting through a system of prices. The level of income, preferences, and prices jointly determine aggregate demand; while the price of inputs and demand for output determines the profitability (and therefore quantity of output) for each firm and sector. The system is subject to constraints and conditions. The system reaches equilibrium through a process of adjustments by consumers and producers to the current price structure.

2.2.4. Law of Diminishing Marginal Utility

It is a law of economics which states that, as a person increases consumption of a product while keeping consumption of other products constant - there is a decline in the marginal utility that the person derives from consuming each additional unit of that product.

For example, say you go to a buffet and the first plate of food you eat is very good. On a scale of 'ten' you would give it a *ten*. Now your hunger has been somewhat tamed, but you get another full plate of food. Since you're not as hungry, your enjoyment rates at a *seven* at best. Most people would stop before their utility drops even more, but say you go back to eat a third full plate of food and your utility drops even more to a *three*. If you kept eating, you would eventually reach a point at which your eating makes you sick, providing dissatisfaction, or dis-utility.

2.3. COST AND REVENUE

2.3.1. Cost curve

Cost curve is the graphical presentation of the costs of production as a function of total quantity produced (Figure 2.4). *Total cost* is the cost of producing some output at some particular rate. *Average cost* is the cost per unit item.

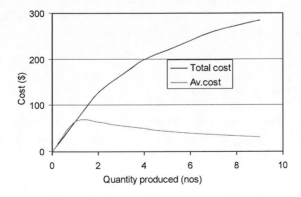

Figure 2.4. Schematic of total and average cost curve.

2.3.2. Revenue or Benefit Curve

Revenue curve or *benefit curve* is the graphical presentation of the revenue obtained from the quantities produced (Figure 2.5).

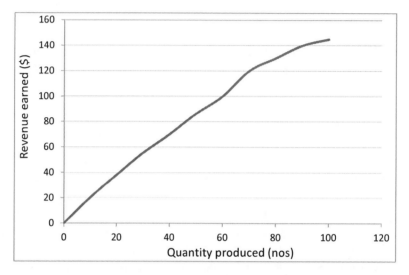

Figure 2.5. Schematic of revenue curve.

2.3.3. Features of Cost Curve

The cost curve (with reference to Industrialal Production System) (Figure 2.6) has several important features:

a) The first is its lower limit, the intercept with the vertical axis, which is associated with design fee, licensee fee, capital cost, insurance, salary of management staffs and security personnel, electric bill for office management unit, and other related fixed costs.

b) The second feature of the cost curve is the slope, which represents the marginal variable costs of production. These include the variable costs such as input/raw-material cost, labour cost, electric bill associated with machine operation, maintenance cost, etc. All such factors are embodied in the slope of the cost function.

2.3.4. Cost and Revenue Function

The relationship between cost and input variable, if mathematically defined, is termed as *cost function*. Similarly, relationship between revenue and input variable is known as *revenue function*. Examples (Industrial production):

a) Cost function

$$Cost (\$) = 800 + (n \times L \times P_L) + (n \times m \times P_i)$$

where
   n = number of machine in operation
   L = number of operators (working days) required for one machine (to operate 24 hrs)
   P_L = unit labor cost ($)
   m = number of input items required for 24 hrs in operation for a machine
   P_i = unit price of input item ($)

b) Revenue function
$$Revenue (\$) = (n \times N_o \times P_o) + (n \times N_b \times P_b)$$

where
   n = number of machine in operation
   N_o = number of quality items produced (output) in 24 hrs per machine
   P_o = unit price of output item ($)
   N_b = number of biproduct in 24 hrs per machine
   P_b = unit price of biproduct item ($)

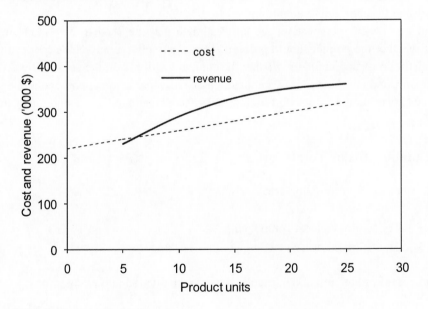

Figure 2.6. Schematic of cost and revenue curve.

2.3.5. Economic Efficiency versus Technical Efficieny

There are two concepts of efficiency relevant to engineering economics: economic efficiency and technical efficiency. Production of a unit of good is considered to be *economically efficient* when that unit of good is produced at the lowest possible cost.

Technical efficiency occurs when it is not possible to increase output without increasing inputs.

Economic efficiency depends on the prices of the factors of production. A key point to understand is the idea that economic efficiency occurs "when the cost of producing a given output is as low as possible". There's a hidden assumption here, and that is the assumption that *all else being equal*. A change that lowers the quality of the good while at the same time lowers the cost of production does not increase economic efficiency. The concept of economic efficiency is only relevant when the quality of goods being produced is unchanged.

Something that is technically efficient may not be economically efficient. The reverse may also be true.

2.4. COST ESTIMATION – IMPORTANCE, COMPONENTS, AND RELEVANT FACTORS

2.4.1. Importance of Cost Estimation

Accurately forecasting the cost of future projects is vital to the survival of any business or organization contemplating future construction. The managers, professional design team members, business owners or construction contractors need cost information to make budgetary and feasibility determinations.

From an Owner's perspective, the cost estimate may be used to determine the project scope or whether the project should proceed. The construction contractor's cost estimate will determine the construction bid or whether the company will bid on the construction contract.

The estimated cost should be accurate enough / reasonable to support economic scrutiny. The cost estimate should be updated from initial gage/estimate to final economic evaluation.

2.4.2. Components of Total Cost

Main steps in cost estimation are:

- To identify the cost components
- To identify approach/technique of cost estimation

Total cost of production of a particular item can be divided into two portions:

- Fixed cost, and
- Variable cost

Fixed Cost

It is the portion of the total cost that requires regardless of the amount of production (small or greater). In other words, fixed costs are those costs which are unaffected (i.e. remain constant) due to change in activity level within the capacity. Examples are – licence fee, rent of the office building, tax and insurance of facilities, administrative and general management salary, guard/security and driver salary, etc. When the capacity is increased by installing plant or industry expansion, the fixed costs may be affected.

Variable Cost

Variable costs are those costs which vary directly with the activity level *or* quantity of output. It increases with the increase in production, and decreases with the decrease in production. Examples are cost of input items (i.e. raw materials for product), labour cost associated with machine operation, interest on running capital, etc.

For economic production process, one must use the least costly combination of inputs for a particular level of output. The optimum mix of output achieves for a given level of benefits at least cost, or in other word, the maximum level of benefit for a given level of cost.

In economic terms, the cost of water has two broad components:

– the cost of its provision [including both fixed (investment) and variable costs (operation and maintenance)], and
– its opportunity cost, or the production value forfeited/offered in alternate use

In addition to fixed & variable cost, and opportunity cost; social cost and environmental cost of the resource should also be taken into account. These costs are real and unavoidable, and someone have to pay - the user, the taxpayer or future generations.

Opportunity Cost

It is monetary advantage/gain of a resource in an alternative use. Under resource limiting condition, opportunity cost need to be considered when comparing alternative options.

In practice, most Farm Accounts do not identify the full cost of agricultural production, probably due to lack of consensus and data on imputed costs, such as family labour, own land, etc. For financial analysis, these items should be estimated at their opportunity cost and be included in cost analysis, in order to identify net income attributed to the project.

Land is an essential factor of agricultural production and in most cases a major cost item. The cost of agricultural products may be significantly increased if planted on high cost land and vice versa. Therefore, land cost must be carefully estimated in all agricultural projects.

If there is a fairly competitive market for land, one may assume that its rent adequately reflects its real cost. However, if there is no market, the cost of land is not easily identifiable. In such cases one needs to estimate its opportunity cost as expressed by the net economic output of current land use.

Other Cost Terminologies

Sometimes, the terms 'initial cost *or* first cost', 'running cost', 'incremental cost', 'recurrent cost', non-recurrent cost', 'direct cost', 'indirect cost', 'junk cost', etc. are used in the literature. But they are not important in financial analysis, as all of these fall within the fixed and variable costs. For convenience, they are defined below.

Initial cost or first cost

It is the installed cost of the asset including purchase price (including tax, if applicable), carrying, installation fees, and other costs (direct and indirect) required to make ready the asset for use/production.

Running cost

It is cost required to operate/run the system and keep in service/production.

Incremental cost

Incremental cost is the additional cost resulting from increasing the output by one unit.

Recurring cost

Recurring costs are repetitive, such as fuel cost.

Non-recurring cost

It is not repetitive, such as capacity building.

Direct cost

Direct costs are those costs which are directly associated with a production output, such as labour, input material cost.

Indirect cost

Those are not directly involved to a specific activity, such as lighting office building, salary of security, etc.

Examples on elements/components of cost of some engineering projects are illustrated in Table 2.1.

Table 2.1. Elements of cost of some engineering projects

Project	Cost elements	
	First cost / Initial cost	*Running cost*
Dam	− Cost for land acquisition (lease/acquire, if needed) − Construction cost − Cost for sluice gate − Installation cost of sluice gate	− Maintenance cost − Salary for sluice gate operator - Opportunity cost of the catchment area (to be flooded) (if applicable)
Hydro-electric power plant	− Cost for dam − Plant/Equipment cost − Delivery charges of the equipments − Import tax (if applicable) − Cost for water intake pipe − Installation and in-house training cost	− Salary of staffs − Maintenance/repair cost − Stand-by generator cost − Upgrading cost (if applicable) − Opportunity cost of the catchment area (to be flooded) (if applicable)
Bridge	− Temporary facility (office, laborer shead, water and electricity) − Soil investigation − Piling, dewatering (if needed) − Material cost	− Maintenance cost

Project	Cost elements	
	First cost / Initial cost	*Running cost*
Agricultural Drainage system	– Survey and design cost – Earth escavation cost – Material cost (pipe and accessories) – Installation cost (laborers)	– Maintenance cost

2.4.3. Elements of a Cost Estimate

Quantity Required

The foundation for a successful estimate relies upon reliable identification (takeoff) of the quantities of the various materials involved in the project.

Labor Hours

Labor hour amounts can be developed by crew analysis or applied on a unit man-hour basis. The use of a labor dollar per unit of work (e.g., $20 per cubic yard for grade beams or $25 per cubic yard for walls) is only applicable when the cost history supports the data being used. The estimator must make allowance for the varying production capability that will occur based upon the complexity of a project.

Labor Rates

The labor rate is the cost per hour for the craftsmen on the project. To determine any craft rate, whether union or open shop, the estimator should start with the basic wages and fringe benefits.

Material Prices

Material prices, especially in today's current market, fluctuate up and down. The estimator must both understand and anticipate the frequency and extent of the price variations and the timing of the buying cycle. Material prices may be affected by:

- purchase at a peak or slack time of the year for the manufacturer
- material availability
- the size of the order
- the delivery timeframe requirement
- physical requirements for delivery, such as distance, road size, or site access
- payment terms and history on previous purchases
- sole-source items
- exchange rates (if the materials are to be imported into the country)

Equipment Costs

Equipment rates depend on the project conditions to determine the correct size or capacity of equipment required to perform the work. When interfacing with other equipment, cycle times and equipment capacity control the costs on the project Costs. This will also differ if the equipment is owned by the contractor as opposed to be rented.

Subcontractor Quotes

A subcontractor quote, like the general estimate, contains labour, material, equipment, indirect costs, and profit. It is dependent upon having the quantities, labour hours, hourly rate, etc., prepared in a reliable manner just like any other part of an estimate. The amount of the subcontractor quote is also dependent upon the payment terms of the contract, and previous payment history between the subcontractor and general contractor. Bonding costs should also be considered.

Indirect Costs

Indirect costs consist of labour, material, and equipment items required to support the overall project.

- *For the owner:* Design fees, permits, land acquisition costs, legal fees, administration costs, etc.
- *For the contractor and subcontractor:* Mobilization, staffing, on-site job office, temporary construction, temporary heating/cooling, and temporary utilities, equipment, small tools and consumables, etc.

Junk Cost

It is the *common cost* for all alternatives. For example, for project evaluation purposes involving alternative use of the same land, the cost of land can be excluded, since it is a common cost item in both the "with" and "without" the project situations.

2.4.4. Approach of Cost Estimation

In engineering projects, and also in industry or business farm, the '*bottom-up*' approach is used to estimate the cost of project. In this approach, at first the cost components and their elements are identified, and then their costs are estimated. Total cost for a particular item is obtained by multiply the number of units by the 'unit cost of the item'. The procedure is followed for all the elements. Then, these costs are summed up to obtain the total direct cost. Then the indirect costs and opportunity costs are identified and estimated.

Total cost = direct costs + indirect costs + opportunity cost

For business/commercial industry, desired profit is added to the total cost to calculate the price of the output/product.

Details of various cost estimation techiques and methods are described in *Chapter 3*.

2.4.5. Factors Affecting Cost and Return

All the cost components can affect the total cost. In addition, the 'time' (due to time value of money) and inflation *or* deflation can affect the total cost of a project.

Similarly, the 'time' and inflation/deflation can affect the total return of a project.

2.4.6. Cost Index

It is the ratio of cost of an item at present time to its cost sometime in the past. The cost of an item can be updated through the use of cost index (CI):

$$CI = C_0 \times \frac{CI_t}{CI_0} \tag{2.1}$$

where

C_t = cost at present time t ($)

C_0 = cost at past time t_0 ($)

CI_t = cost index value at present time t

CI_0 = cost index value at past time t_0

The 'Cost Index (CI)' may be used/applicable in any type of construction works *or* instruments *or* goods and services. The CI may have *seasonality* and *locational* effect, that is, it may vary due to change in season (relevant to labor price or other supply-demand issues) and location (variation in labor cost or transport cost). The two indexes apply to general engineering construction costs: the Construction Cost Index (CCI) and Building Cost index (BCI). Both indexes have a materials and labor component. The CCI can be used where labor costs are a high proportion of total costs. The BCI is more applicable for structures.

2.5. ECONOMIC PRODUCTION STRATEGY IDENTIFICATION: METHODS AND APPLICATIONS

The managers of enterprises or industries are almost constantly making decisions about their business - what product to produce, how much input to use, what combination of inputs to use, how to finance the operation, how and when to sell the product, what selling price should the manager set or accept, etc. Managerial questions relating to production are being made on a continuous basis - should the business hire more workers or lay off some workers in order to increase or decrease output and thereby increase profit, should the business expand its building, should the business invest the capital to purchase new equipment, and again, the list goes on. Mangers need to understand and be able to apply the economic concepts. In this section, we will learn some theory and techniques for maximizing profit from the business/enterprise/industry. Some of the above stated decisions are made on almost a daily basis, e.g., should the business hire more day-workers (often unskilled workers who are willing to work for one day at a time). Other decisions are made occasionally and have a long term impact, e.g., should the business expand the size of the building, or buy new equipment. Not only is this second category of decisions made occasionally, they also take more time to implement (it may take months from the time a manager decides to expand a building until the new space is ready to be used), and the decision is not easily reversed. When managers face such a variety of decisions, such as hiring more day-workers versus deciding whether to expand the building, the time period being considered becomes a factor. In deciding whether to hire more day-workers, the manager knows the decision can be easily changed (i.e., the business can hire a different number of day-workers the next day) and some aspects of the business will remain unchanged (e.g., regardless of how many day-workers are employed, the size of the building and the type of equipment being used will not be changed every day). In deciding whether to expand the building, the manager recognizes that implementing the decision will take time (months or years), the decision is not easily reversed, and there is enough time to change just about every aspect of the production process (e.g., what equipment will be installed in the new building, what energy source will be used, how many workers will be needed to operate the new equipment in the new facility, and the list goes on). The decision about expanding the building could impact the daily operation of the business for years into the future.

2.5.1. Law of Diminishing Marginal Productivity

Concept and Rational

It is a law of economics stating that, as the number of new employees increases, the marginal product of an additional employee will at some point be less than the marginal product of the previous employee. Consider a factory that employs labourers to produce its product. If all other factors of production remain constant, at some point each additional labourer will provide less output than the previous labourer. At this point, each additional employee provides less and less return. If new employees are constantly added, the plant will eventually become so crowded that additional workers actually decrease the efficiency of the other workers, decreasing the production of the factory.

Marginal Product

The marginal product is the change in output that occurs when one more unit of input (such as a unit of labor) is added.

Marginal Revenue

Marginal revenue is the additional revenue that results from producing and selling one more unit of output. Marginal benefit is a measure of the change in benefits over the change in quantity. That is, at each level of production, the marginal benefit refers any additional or reduced benefits incurred for the production of next unit. At low level of production, increase in productivity is easy and marginal cost falling. As production increases, additional gains in productivity becomes smaller, thus marginal cost rises because increasing output becomes more expensive. There may be a level of production where marginal cost is higher than the average cost and the average cost will rise for each unit of production after that point. This type of production function is termed as *diminishing marginal productivity*.

2.5.2. Marginal Cost and Benefit

Marginal Cost

Marginal cost is the additional cost that arises from producing one more unit of output. Marginal cost measures the change in cost over the change in quantity (or activity) (Figure 2.7). That is:

$$M_c = \frac{\Delta C}{\Delta Q} \qquad (2.2)$$

where

M_c = Marginal cost

ΔC = Change in cost corresponding to change in quantity produced

ΔQ = Change in quantity produced

For example, total cost of production for 4 ton wheat in one hectare land is US$500, and it is US$600 for 6 ton. So, we have:

$\Delta C = 600 - 500 = 100$ US$

$\Delta Q = 6 - 4 = 2$ ton

Thus,

$$\frac{\Delta C}{\Delta Q} = \frac{100}{2} = 50 \text{ US\$/t}$$

Marginal cost of production for the next unit produced is US$50.

Mathematically, marginal cost is the ratio of first derivative of cost and quantity supplied, and can be expressed as follows:

$$M_c = \frac{d(TC)}{d(Q)} = \frac{d(FC + VC)}{dQ} = \frac{d(VC)}{dQ} \qquad (2.3)$$

where *TC* is the total cost, *FC* is the fixed cost, *VC* is the variable cost, *Q* is the quantity of an item supplied. Since by definition, the fixed cost do not vary with production quantity, it eliminates from the equation when it is differentiated.

'*Marginal*' indicates the increasing or decreasing costs of production. It allows the producers to evaluate how much they actually pay to produce one more (marginal) unit. At each level of production, the marginal cost refers any additional or reduced costs required to produce the next unit.

Decision rule: Produce additional output as long as revenue from the additional output (MR) exceeds the cost of producing additional output (MC).

Interpretation: A firm will continue to increase the level of output as long as the revenue from the additional output (marginal revenue, MR) is greater than the cost of producing that additional output (marginal cost, MC).

Marginal Value Product (MVP) - additional revenue that results from using one more unit of variable input.

Marginal Input Cost (MIC) - additional cost that arises from using one more unit of variable input.

The marginal revenue product of a resource is defined as the increase in a firm's total revenue attributable to employing one more unit of that resource. The increase in output due to adding one more resource unit is called the marginal product. The marginal revenue product is calculated as the marginal product times the marginal revenue.

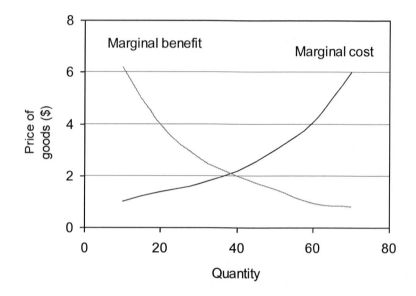

Figure 2.7. Typical marginal cost and marginal benefit curve.

According to the economic theories, the net benefits are maximized up to the point where the benefit added by the last increment of input is equal to the costs of adding that increment of input. An economic system is considered efficient at the point where marginal benefit and marginal cost intersects, or are equal (Figure 2.7).

Due to the law of diminishing returns, we expect that both the marginal product and the marginal revenue product for an input will decline as more of the input is deployed. A firm seeking to maximize profit will increase employment of a variable input unit until the MRP of that input is just equal to what it pays for the input.

Some Relevant Points
- A manager is willing to produce and sell a product as long as the price of the product is equal to or greater than the added cost of producing that product.
- Likewise, a manger will keep on operating the business even though it is incurring a loss as long as the loss incurred by continuing to operate is less than the loss that would be incurred if the business quit operating ($L_{ope} < L_q$).
- In a business where the manager can use two different inputs to produce the output, the manager will use the combination of inputs where the ratio of the productivity of the first input relative to the cost of the first input, equals the ratio of the productivity of the second input relative to the cost of the second input ($P_1/C_1 = P_2/C_2$).

2.5.3. Total Cost and Benefit Curve

The cost and revenue curves help in identifying input conditions for maximizing net benefit. The net benefit is the difference between total cost and total income *or* revenue. That is:

Net benefit = total revenue - total cost

The vertical difference between cost curve and revenue curve represents the *net financial benefit* (Figure 2.8). Maximum net benefit can be determined by constructing cost and revenue curve, and measuring the vertical difference between them. In a free market economy, productively efficient firms use these curves to find the optimal point of production, where they make the profit most.

Figure 2.8. Intersection of total cost and total revenue curve.

2.5.4. Break-Even Point and Break-Even Analysis

Break-Even Point

Break-even point is the number of units that must be sold in order to recover all associated costs, but will produce a profit of zero. In other words, the break-even point is the point at which your product stops costing you money to produce and sell, and starting point to generate a profit for your company.

Break-Even Analysis

It is a tool used to determine when a business will be able to cover all its expenses and begin to make a profit. To calculate your breakeven point you will need to identify your fixed and variable costs. Fixed costs are expenses that do not vary with sales volume, such as rent or administrative salaries. These costs have to be paid regardless of sales and are often referred to as *overhead costs*.

Variable costs vary directly with the sales volume, such as the costs of purchasing inventory, shipping, or manufacturing a product.

Break-even analysis can be used to solve managerial decision problems, such as:

- Setting price level and its sensitivity
- Targeting the "best" value for the variable and fixed cost combinations
- Determining the financial attractiveness of different strategic options for the company

The graphic method of analysis helps in understanding the concept of the break-even point. However, the break-even point can be calculated faster and more accurately with the following formula:

$$B_E = F_C / (U_P - V_C) \tag{2.4}$$

where

B_E = Break-even Point (i.e. Units of production at B_E point)
F_C = Fixed Costs
V_C = Variable Costs per Unit
U_P = Unit Price

Therefore,
Break-Even Point = Fixed Cost / (Unit Price - Variable Unit Cost)

Utilities/Importance of Break-Even Point

Break-even analysis is an important technique for the planning, management and control of business processes. In planning they facilitate an overview of the individual effects of alternative courses of action on a firm's goals. In particular they provide a means of judging and comparing alternatives by reference to satisfying goals or critical goal optimal. Break-even analyses also furnish decision criteria in that they indicate the minimum output volumes below which satisfying levels cannot be attained.

The addition of a time-dimension to break-even analyses is also useful in some cases from the standpoint of managerial intervention. Milestones can then be set as a basis for measuring the profitability of previous activities. When separate break-even analyses are undertaken for each product or product group, weaknesses, and therefore the points at which managerial intervention should begin, become evident.

In the control of the business process, the importance of break-even analysis lies in the fact that it uncovers the strengths and weaknesses of products, product groups or procedures, or of measures in general.

Achieved profit can then be judged by reference to the extent to which actual output deviates from the projected break-even point. The consequential analyses of such a deviation provide information for planning.

Break-even points are the managerial points of the profitability evaluation of managerial action. The planning, management and control of output levels and sales volumes, and of the costs and contribution margins of output levels, constitute the best-known applications.

The importance of preparation in break-even analyses is ultimately reinforced by the fact that the same data can be used for other planning, management and control purposes, for example, budgeting.

The applicability of the results of break-even analysis depends to a large extent upon the reliability and completeness of the input information. If the results of break-even analyses are to be adequately interpreted and used, the following matters in particular must be clearly understood: the implicitly assumed structure of the goods flow; the nature and features of the goals that are to be pursued; the structure of cost, outlay and sales revenue functions.

Costing and Break-Even Analysis

Break-even analysis is decision-making tool. It helps managers to estimate the costs, revenues and profits associated with any level of sales. This can help to decide whether or not to go ahead with a project.

Below the break-even level of output a loss will be made; above this level a profit will be made. Break-even analysis also enables managers to see the impact of changes in price, in variable and fixed costs and in sales levels on the firm's profits.

To ascertain the level of sales required in order to break even, we need to look at how costs and revenues vary with changes in output.

Example of Break-Even Analysis

Mr. John produces and sells Breads from a small shop. The fixed costs per month, including rent of the premises and advertising total, is US$400. The average variable cost of producing a bread is 40 cents and the average selling price of one bread is US$1.0.

The loss is reduced as output rises and he breaks even at 500 breads per month. Any output higher than this will generate a profit for John.

The relationship between costs and revenues is as follows:

Monthly output (Bread)	Fixed cost ($)	Variable cost ($)	Total cost ($, FC + VC)	Total revenue ($)	Profit/loss ($)
0	400	0	400	0	-400
200	400	80	480	240	-240
400	400	160	560	480	-80
450	400	180	580	540	-40
500	400	200	600	600	0
600	400	240	640	720	80
800	400	320	720	960	240
1,000	400	400	800	1200	400

To show this in a graph, plot the total costs and total revenue. It is also normal to show the fixed cost. The horizontal axis measures the level of output. At a certain level of output, the total cost and total revenue curves will intersect. This highlights the break-even level of output (Figure 2.9).

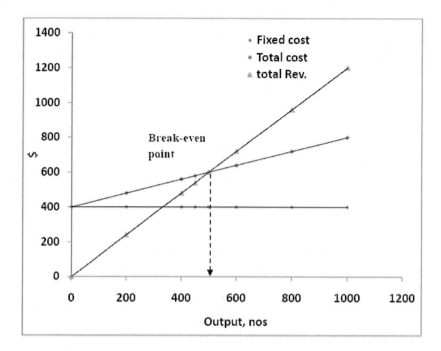

Figure 2.9. Schematic showing of break-even point.

Factors Affecting Break-Even Point

The level of break-even depends on:

- The fixed cost
- The variable cost per unit, and
- The selling price.

The higher the fixed costs, the more the units will have to be sold to break even. The higher the selling price, the fewer units need to be sold.

For some industries, such as the pharmaceutical industry, break even may be at quite high levels of output. Once the new drug has been developed the actual production costs will be low, however, high volumes are needed to cover high initial research and development costs. This is one reason why patents are needed in this industry. The airline and telecommunications industries also have high fixed costs and need high volumes of customers to begin to make profits. In industries where the fixed costs are relatively small and the contribution on each unit is quite high, break-even output will be much lower.

Uses and Limitations of Break-Even for Decision Making

The simple break-even model helps managers analyze the effects of changes in different variables. A manager can easily identify the impact on the break even level of output and the change in profit or loss at the existing output.

However, simple break-even analysis also makes simplifying assumptions; for example, it assumes that the variable cost per unit is constant. In reality this is likely to change with changes in output. As a firm expands, for example, it may be able to buy materials in bulk and benefit from purchasing economies of scale. Conversely, as output rises a firm may have to pay higher overtime wages to persuade workers to work longer hours. In either case, the variable costs per unit are unlikely to stay constant.

Another simplifying assumption of the model is that fixed costs are assumed to remain fixed at all levels of output. In fact, once a certain level of output is reached a firm will have to spend more money on expansion. More machinery will have to be purchased and larger premises may be required, this means that the fixed costs are likely to stepped-function.

To be effective, break-even charts must be updated with addition information (new cost and revenue for higher production) and combined with the manager's own judgment. There are several issues regarding the new output and sell:

- Will a particular output really be sold at this price?
- How will competitors react to change in price or output levels?
- What is likely to happen to costs in the future?

The right decision can only be made if the underlying assumptions of the model are relevant and the manager balances the numerical findings with his or her own experience.

How a Firm Can Reduce Its Break-Even Output?

Firms will be eager to reduce their break-even level of output, as this means they have to sell less to become profitable. To reduce the break-even level of output a firm must do one or more of the following:

- Increase the selling price
- Reduce the level of fixed costs
- Reduce the variable unit cost

2.6. ECONOMIC DECISION TOOLS – COST ANALYSIS

Decision-makers are often faced with the challenges of resource allocation. Resources are scarce; therefore, they must be allocated judiciously. Resource-allocation decisions should be guided by considerations of cost in relation to expected benefits.

Different types of cost analysis are used in program *or* project selection. Cost-effectiveness analysis, cost minimization, cost-benefit analysis, and partial budget analysis represent a continuum of types of cost analysis which can have a place in program evaluation and selection. They range from fairly simple program-level methods to highly technical and specialized methods (e.g. in decision support system). However, all have specialized and technical aspects.

Among the above cost analyses, cost-effectiveness and cost-benefit analysis studies are conducted at a level that involves more than just a local program (such as an individual State Strengthening project). Sometimes they also involve following up over a long period of time, to look at the long-term impact of interventions. They are often used by policy analysts and legislators to make broad policy decisions, so they might look at a large federal program, or compare several smaller pilot programs that take different approaches to solving the same social problem.

It is to be mentioned here that, Cost analyses are evaluation tool, not designed to be used as the sole basis for decision making. Information from such analyses should be incorporated into a specific decision-making framework (see Chapter 1).

2.6.1. Cost-Effectiveness Analysis

Cost-effectiveness analysis (CEA) is used to identify the most cost-effective strategies from a set of options that have similar results. It is a type of economic evaluation used to determine the best use of money to achieve intended objective. It compares different kinds of interventions on the basis of some other common scale for measuring outcomes (i.e. a unit cost or cost per unit of service). In other words, it is a comparison of the relative cost-efficiencies of two or more ways/techniques of performing a task or achieving an objective.

Cost-effectiveness analysis answers how much of a good or service is produced for each dollar spent, or, 'Which of these alternatives is the cheapest or most efficient way to get this benefit?'. This analysis is comparative. This method of economic evaluation is appropriate when the outcomes of different tools/methods/ techniques/ approaches are not equal.

This method enables analysts to compare total costs of activities with their outputs *or* effects, based on differing units of value. The analysis measures costs in monetary terms while measuring outputs in units of goods, services or other effects.

The product of this analysis is cost-effectiveness ratios that represent the trade-off between each program's costs (measured in dollars) and each program's outcomes (measured in appropriate units). The ratio will show for every dollar spent how much achievement is gained or deterioration prevented, depending on the goals of the program. Examples of cost-effectiveness ratios include: cost of water purification (reduction of contaminant) to the reduction level of contaminant; the ratio of costs of a new blood pressure medication to reductions in blood pressure levels among patients; etc. If a new strategy has a low value, it is most "cost effective".

Numerical examples are given at the end of the Chapter (work out problems).

Practical Implications
The concept of cost effectiveness is applied to the planning and management of many types of organized activity (e.g. engineering, medicine, agriculture, military equipment acquisitions, etc.). Cost effectiveness analysis is also applied to many other areas of human activity, including the economics of automobile usage.

In any business or industry setting, a cost-effectiveness analysis can make it much easier to determine which actions will allow the company to achieve a desirable end and generate the most overall benefit as part of the process. The approach can be applied to any portion of the operation, from structuring the management team to settling on the best product delivery options. A properly executed cost-effectiveness analysis can save a company a great deal of money, while also allowing the business to make use of labor, facilities, and other resources to better effect. There is the potential to avoid cost overruns that ultimately lower profits, as well as prevent the accumulation of too much inventory. The right approach to the analysis can even prevent the business from investing money in products or 'the opening of new facilities' that ultimately are not in the best interests of the company.

Shortcomings

Because CEA uses a particular outcome measure that must be common among the programs being considered, its use is limited when the programs have different outcomes.

2.6.2. Cost-Minimization Analysis

An enterprize/business can increase profit by increasing revenue and/or reducing cost. Assuming that the business cannot alter the market price for the output or inputs, the primary way to increase revenue is to increase production; and the primary way to reduce cost is to reduce the quantity of input, or reduce the cost of the production process.

Cost minimization method is appropriate only when different activities have equal outcomes. When the outcomes of two different activities, such as two new medications, are equal, cost-minimization analysis compares the costs of inputs (known collectively in economics as land, labor and capital), usually for the purpose of finding the activity or output with the lowest cost. Cost-minimization analysis is the simplest method of economic evaluation, as it focuses on one side of the equation (costs); however, it has only limited use because it is appropriate only when different activities have equal outcomes.

For example, in concrete works, for a particular strength, different combination of ingredients (input materials) may be sought and checked for lowest/minimum cost. Before conducting a cost-minimization analysis for medical or pharmaceutical therapies, clinical evidence should demonstrate that outcomes between alternative medications or treatments are equal or have only minimal differences.

2.6.3. Cost-Benefit Analysis or Benefit-Cost Analysis

Concept, Analysis, and Decision Making

Cost-benefit analysis is a tool that is widely used by economists to evaluate projects. It basically consists of comparing the total costs of a project with the total benefits. This method of economic evaluation is appropriate when the outcomes or benefits can be valued in monetary term. This provides a common unit of value by which to compare costs and benefits. Cost-benefit analysis usually considers only one program at a time. It is also used to evaluate alternative program/project, but with other indicators (for details, see Chapter 5). The cost-benefit analysis answers the basic questions: "Do the economic benefits of providing this service outweigh the economic costs?" and, "Is it worth doing at all ?"

Cost-benefit analysis is also referred to as benefit-cost analysis by some economists. It weighs the costs and benefits of activities (by attempting to place monetary values on the benefits). Net gain or loss (Nv), is the difference between the two. That is

Nv = Total Benefit − Total Cost

The ratio of benefit to cost is referred to as benefit-cost ratio (BCR), and is expressed as:

$$BCR = \frac{\text{total benefit from the project (in monetary term)}}{\text{total cost involved (in monetary term)}}$$

Both costs and benefits include not only easy-to-quantify monetary items but also other items which can be more difficult to measure, including effects on the environment, public health, safety, etc. (e.g., traffic accidents, effects of exhaust gasses on heart disease, cancer and other diseases, and physical fitness).

Those projects for which the aggregate costs exceed the aggregate benefits (i.e. N_v is negative, or BCR<1) obviously will make society worse off, and should thus be rejected. Among those projects for which the benefits exceed the costs (i.e. N_v is positive, or BCR>1), that with the highest benefit to cost ratios should be selected.

Cost-benefit analysis facilitates to find a good answer to the following type of question: Given the decision-maker's assessment of costs and benefits, which choice should be recommended? Government organizations and public policy analysts employ cost-benefit analysis to determine the desirability of competing policy alternatives. Cost-benefit analysis assists decision makers in assessing projects and activities in economic terms.

Steps

The benefit-cost analysis involves the following general steps:

- Specify a list of all possible courses of actions
- Assign a value (positive or negative) to the outcome for each action, and determine the probability of each outcome
- Compute the expected outcome for each action
- Designate all the positive factors as benefit, and all negative factors as Cost
- Account for the effects of time (for long-term effects/outcomes and costs)
- Sum up costs, and benefits
- Compute the BCR ratio
- Take decision according to decision criteria.

Account for the effects of time - One of the trickiest and most technical aspects of cost-benefit analysis, especially for long-term project studies that follow clients or outcomes over a period of years, is *discounting of costs* and calculating rates of return for alternative uses of the money (such as investing it). This includes taking into account the effects of inflation on the value of the dollar over time, or figuring the depreciation in the value of things like buildings and other capital equipment. Similar issues apply in estimating the value of benefits over a period of time (see Chapter 4 for details).

Shortcomings

Expressing the benefits of activities in monetary terms demonstrates the key shortcoming of cost-benefit analysis. It is difficult—and in some cases, improper—to express some benefits or outcomes in monetary terms. Some may ask what the monetary value is of such benefits as higher academic achievement, increased lifespan or improved domestic security against terrorism.

There are no standard ways to assign dollar values to some qualitative goals, especially in social programs. For example, how do we value things like time, human lives saved, or quality of life? Another aspect is market costs (what people actually pay for something) don't always reflect "real" social costs. For example, sometimes one person's cost is another person's benefit. Also, market costs don't necessarily reflect what economists call the "opportunity costs" of choosing to do one thing instead of another.

Descriptive Example

Suppose as a Production Engineer, you are proposing to purchase an auto-stamping machine having cost of $0.50 Million to increase output. Before you can present the proposal to the Chairman of the company, you need some facts to support your proposal, so you decide to do a cost benefit analysis.

You itemize the benefits. With the new machine, you can produce 150 more units per hour. The two workers currently doing the stamping by hand can be replaced. The units will be higher quality because they will be more uniform. You are convinced these outweigh the costs.

There is a cost to purchase the machine and it will consume some electricity. Any other costs would be insignificant. You calculate the selling price of the 150 additional units per hour multiplied by the number of production hours per month. Add to that two percent for the units that aren't rejected (which occurs in manual) because of the quality of the machine output. You also add the monthly salaries of the two workers. That's the total benefit.

Then you calculate the monthly cost of the machine, by dividing the purchase price by 12 months per year and divide that by the 8 years the machine should last. The manufacturer's specification tell you what the power consumption of the machine is, and you can get power cost numbers from accounting so you figure the cost of electricity to run the machine and add the purchase cost to get a total cost figure. You subtract your total cost figure from your total benefit value and your analysis will show a healthy profit.

2.6.4. Partial and Full Budget Analysis

A budget is a formal quantitative expression of plans on production inputs and outputs. Budgets indicate the type, quality, and quantity of production resources or inputs needed, and the type, quality, and quantity of output or product obtained. Two types of budgets are used in industry/farm/business:

- Whole-farm budget / Full budget
- Partial budget

2.6.4.1. Partial Budget Analysis

Many changes proposed by a farm/industry/manager on a business affect only part of the business. Therefore, a complete farm budget is not needed to determine the profitability of the specific changes in the operations of the farm/business. You can accomplish this in organized fashion, by using the *partial budget*.

Partial budgeting is a planning and decision-making framework/methodology by which a business/production manager assesses whether a change in production practices will increase or decrease profit. *It only addresses those parts of the business that will be impacted by the change.* It focuses only on the changes in income (benefits) and expenses (costs) that would result from implementing a specific alternative. Thus, all aspects of farm profits that are unchanged by the decision can be safely ignored.

A partial budget analysis does not determine profitability of the farm; it only determines the "*change in profit*" if an alternative is adopted; i.e., even though the change may enhance profit, the enterprise or overall business may still be incurring an operating loss. In preparing a partial budget analysis, only the parts of the business that will change if the alternative is adopted, are considered in the analysis. The aspects of the business that will not be affected by the alternative are not considered because they will remain the same whether or not the change is made. For example, if a business is to shift from one enterprise to another enterprise (or, one production system to another), a partial budget analysis will reveal whether the shift will increase or decrease profit. The partial budget analysis will *not* reveal whether the original enterprise was profitable, whether the alternative enterprise is profitable, or whether the overall business is profitable. The analysis will only reveal 'how the level of profit will change if the alternative is adopted'.

Points to be considered in partial budget analysis:

- In preparing a partial budget analysis, consider preparing a short list of inputs that will not be changed whether or not the alternative is adopted. Preparing this brief list of "unaffected" may help minimize the error of overlooking some aspect of the business that might be impacted by a decision about the alternative being considered.
- Opportunity cost is a consideration in preparing a partial budget. If adopting the alternative changes how the manager uses his or her own assets (such as their own labor or capital), the impact of that change needs to be considered in the analysis as an opportunity cost. For example if adopting alternative production technology reduces the amount of time the manager needs to commit to the enterprise, that reduction of labor is a positive impact and must be included in the analysis as a cost saving.
- Non-economic considerations must be taken into account when considering an alternative. Such considerations may include the social aspects of having less labor on the farm, increased/decreased leisure time, the need for increased or specialized knowledge, and safety and/or ease of use of equipment. Note that these are generally focused on quality of life measures, which are frequently difficult to quantify

Steps in Partial Budget Analysis

Steps for partial budget analysis can be summarized as follows:

a) State the proposed change
b) Identify and list down the added returns
c) Identify and list down the reduced costs

d) Identify and list down the reduced returns

e) Identify and list down the added costs

f) Summarize the net effect

Positive effect = added return (from existing practice) + reduced cost (from existing practice)

Negative effect = reduced return (from existing practice) + added cost (from existing practice)

Net effect = Positive effect − Negative effect

Ensuring Realistic Estimates

A decision based on partial budget analysis is only as good as the information used in the analysis will allow. There are several ways to ensure that you are using realistic and accurate figures for price savings and expenses in your analyses:

- review previous years' actual expenses
- use the Internet to search fees associated with services
- get prices from several suppliers
- talk with other producers who use the alternative you are considering

By speaking with farm managers or producers who already made a change similar to what you are considering, you can also learn about things they wish they had done differently, problems they encountered, or successes they achieved.

Relationship between Partial Budget and Full Budget (Profitability) Analysis

A manager could prepare two enterprise analyses; one for the original enterprise and one for the alternative, and then compare the profitability of each enterprise. The difference between the profitability of the two enterprises should be the same as the change in profit calculated by the partial budget analysis. Thus, there is a relationship between enterprise analysis and partial budget analysis. A partial budget could be described as "a summary of the differences between two enterprise analyses of alternative activities."

2.6.4.2. Full Budget Analysis

In this analysis, total cost and benefit of production are considered for cost and benefit estimation, respectively. A full budget analysis determines profitability of a production system (or business), thus "*change in profit*" of an alternative can be evaluated (as described in relationship).

Impact of Subsidies on Budget Analysis (Or Profitability Analysis)

"Subsidies" are sometimes granted in order to support current agricultural policies. These are temporary cash injections, influencing production decisions, but external to the financial mechanism and identity of production. It is important to isolate the effect of subsidies by entering these amounts at the bottom of Profit and Loss accounts. However, this is scrutinizing the real economic characteristics of production and impairs the most important financial indices.

2.7. PROFITABILITY ANALYSIS

2.7.1. Concept

Production theory is based on the assumption that business managers strive to make decisions to maximize profit. Looking at a company's profitability is a very important step in understanding a company. Profitability is essentially why the company exists and is a key component while deciding to invest or to stay invested in a company.

In the profit or income statement, there are different levels of "profit" *or* "profit margins" in use - gross profit, operating profit, pretax profit and net profit. Basically, profit is the amount of money (at the gross, operating, pretax or net income level) generated by the company as a percent of the sales generated. The objective of margin analysis is to detect consistency or positive/negative trends in a company's earnings.

2.7.2. Methods of Analysis

There are many metrics involved in calculating profitability – Total profit, Profitability Ratios, Cash Flow, Earnings and Earnings Growth, Profit Margins etc.

2.7.2.1. Net Profit
a) **Cost and revenue approach**

Net profit = Total revenue – Total cost

Net profit amount is obtained by subtracting the sum of the company's expenses (operating and others) from the total profit amount. Generally, operating expenses would include such account captions as selling, marketing and administrative, research and development, depreciation and amortization, rental properties, etc.

b) **Benefit-Cost ratio (BCR) approach**

This approach is applicable when the project is short-term (1 year or around) and the BCR is known (e.g. benefit is added to the price of the item, i.e. price = production cost + benefit). The profit (also termed as *total net profit*) is calculated as:

$$Profit = (BCR - 1) \times Cost \tag{2.5}$$

Here, "*Cost*" indicates total cost involved in the project. If the result is negative (-), it indicates 'Loss'.

c) NPV approach

This approach is applicable when the benefit of the project continues for a long period (and the 'Cost' may either continue for a long or not), and the BCR is not known.

The profit is calculated as:

$$Profit \ = \ (NPV_b - NPV_c) \tag{2.6}$$

where

NPV_b = Net present value of the benefits
NPV_c = Net present value of the cost(s)

2.7.2.2. Earnings and Earnings Growth
Earnings = sales × profit margin

For example, the earnings of "Karim Textile Ltd." are illustrated below:
• 2011: $13.0 billion x 7.2% = $936 million
• 2012: $13.6 billion x 7.0% = $952 million

Earnings increased from $936 million in 2011 to $952 million in 2012 or by 1.71%.

Earnings per share = net income/shares outstanding

Long-term historical look at earnings growth

• 2007 : $ 1100 million, 2% decrease over 2006
• 2008 : $1050 million, 4.55% decrease
• 2009 : $1000 million, 4.76% decrease
• 2010 : $936 million, 6.4% decrease
• 2011 : $952 million, 1.71% increase
• 2012 : $960 million, 0.84% increase

In analyzing the above earnings growth over the past six years, we can see that the company has been ≥$1000 million earnings mark for the early 3 years. Over the six years, the company has averaged earnings growth of - 2.53%.

2.7.2.3. Gross Profit
Gross Profit = Total sales - cost of sales

When analyzing a company, gross profit is very important because it indicates how efficiently management uses labor and supplies in the production process. More specifically, it can be used to calculate gross profit margin.

2.7.2.4. Gross Profit Margin
Gross Profit Margin = Gross Income / Sales

The gross profit margin is a measurement of a company's manufacturing and distribution efficiency during the production process. The gross profit tells an investor the percentage of revenue/ sales left after subtracting the cost of goods sold. A company that boasts a higher gross profit margin than its competitors, is more efficient. Investors tend to pay more for businesses that have higher efficiency ratings than their competitors, as these businesses should be able to make a decent profit as long as overhead costs are controlled (overhead refers to rent, utilities, etc.)

If a company's gross income and sales for year 2011 are $11.5 and $12.0 billion, then gross profit margin (GPM) for that year is:

$11.5 billion / $12.0 billion = 95.8%

If the GPM for the year 2012 is 90%, it implies that the company is less efficient in its production process and distribution than the previous year (as the gross profit margin decreased).

2.7.2.5. Operating Income
Operating income = Total sales - operating expenses

The amount of profit realized from a businesses operations after taking out operating expenses, such as cost of goods sold (COGS) or wages and depreciation. Operating income takes the gross income (revenue minus COGS) and subtracts other operating expenses and then removes depreciation. These operating expenses are costs that are incurred from operating activities and include things such as office supplies and heat and power.

- 2010: $4.2 billion
- 2011: $4.0 billion

2.7.2.6. Operating Margin
Operating Margin = operating income / total sales

Operating margin is a measure of what proportion of a company's revenue is left over after paying for variable costs of production such as wages, raw materials, etc. A healthy operating margin is required for a company to be able to pay for its fixed costs, such as interest on debt.

If a company's margin is increasing, it is earning more per dollar of sales. The higher the margin, the better.

- 2010: $4.2 billion / $12.5 billion = 33.6 %
- 2011: $4.0 billion / $13.3 billion = 30.0 %

As Operating Margin has decreased, it leaves less cash for the company to pay for its fixed costs. As the operating margin decreased, the company does not pass this metric.

2.7.2.7. Net Profit Margin

Net Profit Margin = Net income / total sales

It is a ratio of profitability calculated as net income divided by revenues, or net profits divided by sales. It measures how much out of every dollar of sales a company actually keeps in earnings.

Profit margin is very useful when comparing companies in similar industries. A higher profit margin indicates a more profitable company that has better control over its costs compared to its competitors. Profit margin is displayed as a percentage; a 15% profit margin, for example, means the company has a net income of $0.15 for each dollar of sales.

2.7.2.8. Profitability Ratios

a) *Return on investment (or Capital Assets) (ROI) = Net income / total assets*

ROI is an indicator of how profitable a company is relative to its total assets. ROI gives an idea as to how efficient management is at using its assets to generate earnings. Calculated by dividing a company's net income by its total assets, ROI is displayed as a percentage. Sometimes this is referred to as "return on investment."

- 2010 : $936 million / $22000 million = 4.25 %
- 2011 : $952 million / $23000 million = 4.14 %

As the ROA decreased from 4.25 % in 2010 to 4.14 % in 2011, it implies that management was less efficient in using its assets to generate earnings. Waste Management does not pass.

b) Return on Equity (ROE) = Net income / shareholder's equity

The amount of net income returned as a percentage of shareholders equity. Return on equity measures a corporation's profitability by revealing how much profit a company generates with the money shareholders have invested.

- 2010 : $936 million / $6300 million = 14.9 %
- 2011 : $952 million / $6200 million = 15.4 %

As the ROE increased from 14.9 % in 2010 to 15.4 % in 2011, it reveals that the company is generating more profits from the money shareholders have invested.

2.7.2.9. Cash Flows

Free Cash Flow = operating cash flow - capital expenditure

It is a measure of financial performance calculated as operating cash flow minus capital expenditures. Free cash flow (FCF) represents the cash that a company is able to generate after laying out the money required to maintain or expand its asset base. Free cash flow is important because it allows a company to pursue opportunities that enhance shareholder value. Without cash, it's tough to develop new products, make acquisitions, pay dividends and reduce debt.

It is important to note that negative free cash flow is not bad in itself. If free cash flow is negative, it could be a sign that a company is making large investments. If these investments earn a high return, the strategy has the potential to pay off in the long run.

- 2010 : $2.3 billion - $1.0 billion = $1.3 billion
- 2011 : $2.5 billion - $1.3 billion = $1.2 million

As the final number in free cash flow fell by 2.2%, this is inline with most of the analysis as many of the numbers are slowly declining. As the number is still positive it implies that the company has enough cash to develop new products, make acquisitions, pay dividends and reduce debt.

Cash flow margin = Cash flow from operating activities / total sales

The higher the percentage, the more cash is available from sales. If a company is generating a negative cash flow, which would show up as a negative number in the numerator in the cash flow margin equation, then even as it is generating sales revenue, it is losing money. The company will have to borrow money or raise money through investors in order to keep on operating.

If the company's cash flow margin is positive, it does not have to borrow money or raise money to keep operating.

2.7.2.10. Selling Expense as a Percentage of Total Sale
SGandA % Sales = SGandA / total sales

Reported on the income statement, it is the sum of all direct and indirect selling expenses and all general and administrative expenses of a company.

High SGandA expenses can be a serious problem for almost any business. Examining this figure as a percentage of sales or net income compared to other companies in the same industry can give some idea of whether management is spending efficiently or wasting valuable cash flow.

2.8. PRICE INDICES

Different types of price indices are in use: Consumer Price Indexes (CPI), Supplier Price Index (SPI), Living Cost Index, Food Price Index, etc. The price indices may have *seasonality* and *locational* effect, that is, it may vary due to change in season (relevant to labor price or other supply-demand issues) and location (variation in labor cost, production cost or transport cost).

Price indices have several potential uses. For particularly broad indices, the index can be said to measure the economy's price level *or* a cost of living. More narrow price indices can help producers with business plans and pricing. Sometimes, they can be useful in helping to guide investment.

2.8.1. Consumer Price Index (CPI)

Consumer Price Index (CPI) measures changes in the prices paid by consumers for a representative basket of goods and services. The CPI can be developed for different locations (and also for rural and urban) and different types of consumers.

$$CPI = \frac{C_t}{C_0} = \frac{\Sigma(p_{c,t_n} \times q_c)}{\Sigma(p_{c,t_0} \times q_c)} \tag{2.7}$$

where
C_t = price of a representative basket of goods and services at present time t ($)
C_0 = price of similar representative basket of goods and services at past time t_0 ($)
p_c = price of an item ($)
q_c = quantity of the item

The CPI represents change in consumer goods and services purchased by households. It is a statistical estimate constructed using the prices of a sample of representative items whose prices are collected periodically.

2.8.2. Supplier Price Index (SPI)

The Supplier Price Index (SPI) measures changes in the prices achieved by suppliers for a representative basket of goods and services. The SPI can also be developed for different locations and different qualities of good and services.

$$CPI = \frac{C_t}{C_0}. \tag{2.8}$$

where

C_t = price of a representative basket of goods and services at present time t ($)
C_0 = price of similar representative basket of goods and services at past time t_0 ($)

2.8.2. Living Cost Index

The Living Cost Index (LCI) is the most reliable source of city-to-city comparisons of key consumer costs available anywhere. Accurate and reliable cost of living comparisons can be made between an area and any other participating cities across the States or among international cities.

$$LCI = \frac{C_t}{C_b} \qquad\qquad (2.9)$$

where

C_t = cost of living (with defined standard) in a target city ($)
C_b = cost of living (with same defined standard) at a base city ($)

2.8.3. Food Price Index

The FAO (Food and Agricultural Organization of the United Nations) *Food Price Index* is a measure of the monthly change in international prices of a basket of food commodities. It consists of the average of five commodity group price indices (representing 55 quotations), weighted with the average export shares of each of the groups.

2.9. FACTORS AFFECTING VALUE OF MONEY

The factors affecting value of money include:

- Time
- Interest rate
- Inflation/deflation
- Local/regional/international economy
- Supply of goods/services and their price
- Supply of goods and/or services and their price temporarily increase or decrease the value of money (called temporary effect *or* local effect).

2.9.1. Time Factor

Value of money is influenced by time. We all will agree that 100 dollar today is better than 120 dollar 20 years later. Times makes money from the money, if it is invested properly. Knowing the interest rate, value of money can be estimated using the following formula:

$$FV = PV(1 + i)^N \qquad\qquad (2.10)$$

where

FV = future value (of present money, PV) after N years
PV = present value
i = interest rate
N = number of year

2.9.2. Inflation

Definition
Inflation is defined as a sustained increase in the general level of prices for goods and services. It is the rate at which the general level of prices for goods and services is rising, and, subsequently, purchasing power is falling. It is measured as an annual percentage increase.

Impacts of Inflation
As inflation rises, every dollar you own buys a smaller percentage of a good or service. For example, if the inflation rate is 2%, then a $1 pack of gum will cost $1.02 in a year. Central banks attempt to stop severe inflation, along with severe deflation, in an attempt to keep the excessive growth of prices to a minimum.

The value of a dollar does not stay constant when there is inflation. The value of a dollar is observed in terms of purchasing power, which is the real, tangible goods that money can buy. When inflation goes up, there is a decline in the purchasing power of money. For example, if the inflation rate is 2% annually, then theoretically a $1 pack of gum will cost $1.02 in a year. After inflation, your dollar can't buy the same goods it could beforehand.

Causes of Inflation
In the long run, sustained growth in the money supply relative to the growth of the productive capacity of the economy will create inflation.

There is no single cause that is universally agreed upon, but at least two theories are generally accepted:

Demand-Pull Inflation - This theory can be summarized as "too much money chasing too few goods". In other words, if demand is growing faster than supply, prices will increase. This usually occurs in growing economies.

Cost-Push Inflation - When companies' costs go up, they need to increase prices to maintain their profit margins. Increased costs can include things such as wages, taxes, or increased costs of imports.

2.9.3. Deflation

A general decline in prices, often caused by a reduction in the supply of money or credit, is termed as deflation. This is the opposite of inflation.

Deflation can be caused also by a decrease in government, personal or investment spending. The deflation has the side effect of increased unemployment since there is a lower level of demand in the economy, which can lead to an economic depression. Central banks attempt to stop severe deflation, along with severe inflation, in an attempt to keep the excessive drop in prices to a minimum.

Declining prices, if they persist, generally create a vicious spiral of negatives such as falling profits, closing factories, shrinking employment and incomes, and increasing defaults on loans by companies and individuals. To counter deflation, the Federal Reserve can use monetary policy to increase the money supply and deliberately induce rising prices, causing inflation.

Rising prices provide an essential lubricant for any sustained recovery because businesses increase profits and take some of the depressive pressures off wages and debtors of every kind.

2.10. TAX CALCULATION FOR INCOME

2.10.1. Concept of 'Income Tax' and 'Depreciation Cost'

For individuals, private farm, or corporation, the income is taxable. Tax rate for each country/state varies, normally incremental tax rate with the increase in income. For public (Govt.) works or projects, income/revenue is not taxable.

In many, annual depreciation is tax deductable (termed as 'tax depreciation'). Tax depreciation is deducted from the income when computing tax. Tax depreciation must be calculated following government approved method/rules/guidelines.

The tax code of many industrialized countries allows tax payers deductions for depreciation of capital items (the assets of the industry/ company/corporation) on both individual and corporate tax returns. Tax deductable depreciation may be named and calculated in different ways in different countries (such as "capital cost allowance" in Canada).

In the context of 'depreciation cost' (specially for income tax purposes – calculating tax deductible depreciation), the term 'Cost recovery period' is often used. It is the amount of time that takes for an asset to depreciate from its purchase price to its salvage value. In other words, the cost recovery period is an amount of time equal to the useful life of the asset. In most cases, recovery period applies to a business owner that invests in a business by purchasing a capital asset. For intangible assets (not physical assets, refer to things like patents and copyrights), the term "Amortization" is used.

For example, the purchase of a machine or the construction of a building would qualify as a capital asset in many countries.

The taxation rule allows you to depreciate the costs of these assets over time. This depreciation counts as a deduction on your itemized tax return (based on country's tax rule/guide).

Tax for Imported Items

Tax may also be charged on imported (foreign) items for capital item or operating inputs. In that case, the price or cost of the item should be taken as the sum of actual/cited price and tax.

2.10.2. Calculation of Income Tax

Tax should be calculated on '*taxable income*'. 'Depreciation' of the capital items is a cost, and that should be deducted from the gross income.

Taxable income = gross income – depreciation

Table 2.2. Tax rate in Malaysia (for the year 2010) (LHDN, Malaysia, 2010)

Income range (MYR)	Income amount/fragmentation	Tax (MYR)	
		Based on rate (%)	Lump sum
0 – 2500	Up to 2500	0	0
2,501 – 5,000	2500	1	-
5,001 – 10,000	First 5,000	-	25
	Next 5,000	3	-
10,001 - 20,000	First 10,000	-	175
	Next 10,000	3	-
20,001 - 35,000	First 20,000	-	475
	Next 15,000	7	-
35,001 - 50,000	First 35,000	-	1525
	Next 15,000	12	-
50,001 - 70,000	First 50,000	-	3325
	Next 20,000	19	-
70,000 – 100,000	First 70,000	-	7175
	Next 30,000	24	-
Over 100,000	First 100,000	-	14325
	Next	26	-

The 'depreciation' amount must be calculated following the rules and guidelines of the respective Province or State. However, the 'depreciation' allowance for *income tax purposes* may not reflect the actual use of the machine. Accordingly, it is a common recommendation that businesses maintain two depreciation schedules - one that complies with income tax law, and another that more accurately allocates the cost of the machine over its useful life. In managing depreciation for tax purposes, the manager will strive to make decisions, as allowed by Federal/State income tax law, to maximize the business' after-tax income. For *management purposes* (termed as 'Book depreciation'), the manager will strive to develop and follow a depreciation method that results in an accurate statement of costs and net income, without income tax considerations. Sample example of incremental tax rate in Malaysia (2010) is given in Table 2.2.

2.11. Valuation of Assets - Salvage Value, Economic Life, Depreciation, Depletion

2.11.1. Salvage Value

It is the estimated sale value (market value) of an asset (property/ equipment/machine) at the end of its effective (or economic or useful) life. It is the money that can be gained by selling the hardware or instruments. Salvage value is sometimes referred to as "*residual value*". The value is used in accounting to determine depreciation amounts, and in the tax system to determine deductions.

In conjunction with the purchase price and accounting method, it is used to determine the amount by which an asset depreciates each period. For example, with a straight-line basis, an asset that cost $10,000 and has a salvage value of $2,000 and a useful life of ten (10) years would be depreciated at $800 each year [($10,000-$2,000)/10yrs = $800/year)\.

2.11.2. Economic Life

Concept

'Effective life' *or* 'effective service life' *or* 'economic life' *or* 'economic service life' is the life-span (number of years) of an asset or goods during which it can provide its intended service/production with economic efficiency (i.e. reasonable service/production without much maintenance or updating cost).

Calculation of Economic Life

In numeric term, it is the number of years up to the minimum annual worth (AW) of costs (Figure 2.10).

Total AW of costs = Capital recovery +
AW of annual operating cost   (2.11)

As it is cost (i.e. to represent negative income), in many texts it is represent by negative (-) sign.

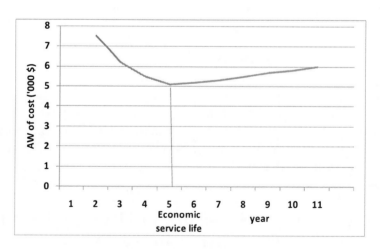

Figure 2.10. Schematic showing of economic service life.

Normal Economic Life of Common Engineering Structures

Ideal/average *effective life* of different engineering structures is given Table 2.3.

Table 2.3. Effective life of some engineering structures/equipents

Structure	Economic life (years)
RCC road	15-18
Asphalt/bituminous road	18 - 20
RCC bridge	75 - 100
Brick/cement-concrete irrigation canal	15 – 25
RCC building	75 – 100
Water supply pump	25– 40

2.11.3. Book Depreciation

2.11.3.1. Concept

Depreciation means reduction in value of an asset due to age and/or uses. After some uses, the originality of an asset (e.g. building, instrument, car, etc.) is decreased, and consequently the value is decreased.

For cost comparison purposes, depreciation is simply the amount by which an asset decreases in value over some period of time. For example, if you bought a piece of equipment for $20,000 and sold it for $6,000 after seven years of service, you would say that the depreciation during the seven-year period was $20,000 minus $6,000, or $14,000. This $14,000 was one of your costs of owning the equipment for that period.

Book depreciation is used by company, corporation, organization, and business-farm for their internal financial accounting. It is the reduction of value/price of the asset based upon the usages pattern and effect/productive life of the asset.

To calculate depreciation, we need to know certain things about the asset or equipment:

(1) its first cost,
(2) its estimated service life, and
(3) its expected salvage value.

The difference between the first cost and the salvage value will represent the amount by which the equipment will depreciate during its life - that is, during the time you expect to use it.

2.11.3.2. Calculation of Book Depreciation

For the purposes of management (not for tax purpose), 'Depreciation' is a system or procedure to allocate or assign a portion of the cost of an asset to each production period during which the asset is used. There are many different methods of writing-off cost. One common way of classifying depreciation accounting method is:

One common way of classifying depreciation accounting method is:

a) Methods that aim to give a greater write-off in the early years of life than in the final years of life such as declining- balance method, the sum of-the-digits method, Multiple straight-line method.

b) Methods that aim to give a uniform write-off through out the entire service life, straight line method.
c) Methods that aim to give a smaller write-off in the early years of life than in the final, sinking-fund method.

1) Declining-Balance Depreciation Accounting

It is common practice for assets to be used as stand-by or inferior uses during their final years of their lives. Due to this their contribution is decreased. Equally the writing-off also is made to decrease by using the declining-balance depreciation method. In declining-balance depreciation method a given depreciation rate is applied each year to the remaining portion of the cost of the asset (book value). For example, if a 10% rate is applied to an asset that costs $35000 first year depreciation will be $35000 x 0.1=$3500. The second year cost will be (35000-3500) x 0.1 = $3150, and the third year cost will be (35000-3500-3150)x0.1 = $2835 and so on.

2) Sum of- the-Years-Digits Deprecation Accounting

In this method, the digits corresponding to the number of years of estimated life are added together. For example, considering a machine having estimated life of 20 years, initial cost of $35000, and salvage value of $3500 the sum of the digits from 1 to 20 is 210. The depreciation charge for the first year is 20/210 of the ($35000-$3500) and in the second year the depreciation charge is 19/210 of ($35000-$3500) and so on. This method writes-off about $3/4^{th}$ of the depreciable cost in the first half of the estimated life.

3) Sinking-Fund Depreciation Accounting

In this approach, a real or imaginary sinking fund is established and a fixed deposit is made in the fund at the end of each year (annual depreciation cost) in the life of the asset. The deposit is so computed that the amount put into the fund plus the interest earned on it will just equal the amount by which the asset is to be depreciated. The amount in the fund at the end of the life period is to be equal to the depreciated value of the equipment or the difference between first cost and salvage value.

Sinking-fund amount = First cost – salvage value

Annual depreciation cost = [sinking-fund amount] x $\left[\dfrac{i}{(i+i)^{n}-1}\right]$.   (2.12)

where,   i = Interest rate
           n = Estimated service life

When the rates of interest approaches zero, the sinking fund method yields the straight line method.

4) Straight-Line Depreciation Accounting

Straight-Line depreciation method is the most conservative practice in evaluating the depreciation cost in economic studies. According to this method, the value of an asset decreases linearly with time. That is, the annual depreciation amount is constant throughout its effective life *or* recovery period. If the first cost is F ($), salvage value is S ($), and the effective life is *n* years, then the annual depreciation amount (or annual rate) according to straight line method, D_{SL} ($ per year) is:

$$D_{SL} = \frac{F-S}{n} \qquad (2.13)$$

= (Initial cost - Salvage value)/ estimated service life in years

The term $1/n$ is termed as depreciation factor (d).
From the above equation, book value of an asset after *t* yr,

$$BV_t = F - \left(\frac{F-S}{n}\right) \times t \qquad (2.14)$$

Features of SL method

It is a constant rate (linear), non-accelerated model
Easy to understand and calculate
An estimated salvage value of the asset is always considered

Out of the above methods, '*straight line method*' is commonly used. It is the basic method, and others methods are compared/validated against this method.

2.11.4. Depletion

The term 'depletion' is used (*instead of 'depreciation'*) in case of natural resources/deposits such as forest, groundwater, coal, geothermal deposits, etc. Two types of depletion are in use:

- Cost depletion, and
- Percentage depletion.

Cost Depletion
Cost depletion depends on the usages, not time (as in depreciation). Cost depletion factor (p_t) for a particular year t, is:

$$p_t = \frac{first\ cost}{resource\ capacity\ or\ availability} \qquad (2.15)$$

Annual depletion cost,

$$A_t = p_t \times (year's\ usage\ volume). \qquad (2.16)$$

If the resource availability of the asset is re-estimated after some year of starting depletion, a revised or new cost depletion factor is determined based on the revised cost and resource capacity/availability.

Percent Depletion

According to this approach, a fixed percentage of the resource's gross income is depleted.

$$Percent\ depletion\ amount = percent \times gross\ income\ from\ property \qquad (2.17)$$

2.12. SOME RELEVANT ECONOMIC TERMINOLOGIES

2.12.1. GDP (Gross Domestic Product)

It is the monetary value of all the finished goods and services produced within a country's borders in a specific time period, though GDP is usually calculated on an annual basis. It includes all of private and public consumption, government outlays, investments and exports less imports that occur within a defined territory.

$$GDP = C + G + I + NX . \qquad (2.18)$$

where

"C" is equal to all private consumption, or consumer spending, in a nation's economy
"G" is the sum of government spending
"I" is the sum of all the country's businesses spending on capital
"NX" is the nation's total net exports, calculated as total exports minus total imports.
NX = Exports - Imports

Two different approaches are used to calculate GDP. In theory, the amount spent for goods and services should be equal to the income paid to produce the goods and services, and other costs associated with those goods and services. Calculating GDP by adding up expenditures is called the expenditure approach (above eqn.).

Another approach is to compute GDP by examining income for resources (sometimes referred to as gross domestic income, or GDI), termed as the resource cost/income approach.

2.12.2. Gross National Product (GNP)

It is an economic statistic/indicator that includes GDP, plus any income earned by residents from overseas investments, minus income earned within the domestic economy by overseas residents.

GNP is a measure of a country's economic performance, or what its citizens produced (i.e. goods and services) and whether they produced these items within its borders.

GNP = GDP + resident's overseas earns –
overseas resident's earn within country   (2.19)

2.12.3. Economic Growth Rate

It is a measure of economic growth from one period to another in percentage terms. This measure does not adjust for inflation, it is expressed in nominal terms. In practice, it is a measure of the rate of change that a nation's gross domestic product goes through from one year to another.

Gross national product can also be used if a nation's economy is heavily dependent on foreign earnings.

$$Economic\ Growth\ Rate = \frac{GDP_2 - GDP_1}{GDP_1}.$$ (2.20)

The economic growth rate provides insight into the general direction and magnitude of growth for the overall economy.

In the United States, for example, the long-term economic growth rate is around 2-5%, this lower rate is seen in most highly industrialized countries. Fast-growing economies, on the other hand, see rates as high as 10% although this rate of growth is not likely to be sustainable over the long term.

2.12.4. Real Economic Growth Rate

A measure of economic growth from one period to another expressed as a percentage and adjusted for inflation (i.e. expressed in real as opposed to nominal terms). The real economic growth rate is a measure of the rate of change that a nation's gross domestic product (GDP) experiences from one year to another.

Gross national product (GNP) can also be used if a nation's economy is heavily dependent on foreign earnings. The real economic growth rate builds onto the economic growth rate by taking into account the effect that inflation has on the economy. The real economic growth rate is a "constant dollar" and is therefore a more accurate look at the rate of economic growth because it is not distorted by the effects of extreme inflation or deflation.

2.12.5. Real Gross Domestic Product (GDP)

An inflation-adjusted measure that reflects the value of all goods and services produced in a given year, expressed in base-year prices. Often referred to as "constant-price", "inflation-corrected" GDP or "constant dollar GDP". Unlike nominal GDP, real GDP can account for changes in the price level, and provide a more accurate figure. Let's consider an example.

Say in 2011, nominal GDP is $200 billion. However, due to an increase in the level of prices from 2006 (the base year) to 2011, real GDP is actually $170 billion. The lower real GDP reflects the price changes while nominal does not.

2.13. WORKOUT PROBLEMS

Example 2.1.

Cost of production for 15 ton steel bar is US$4450, and it is US$5550 for 14 ton. What is the marginal cost of production of steel bar?

Solution:
We have: $\Delta Q = 15 - 14 = 1$ ton
$\Delta C = 5550 - 4450 = 1100$ US$

Thus, $= 1100$ US$/ton
Marginal cost of production for the next unit produced is US$1100. (**Ans.**)

Example 2.2.

An engineering project is proposed to implement. The following elemental costs (in present value) are estimated ('000 $):

Instrument cost = 92
Instrument installation and training = 4.2
Indirect costs = 12
Operation and maintenance cost for the effective life = 40
Opportunity cost of the land resource = 5
Determine the total cost of the proposed project.

Solution:
We get
Total cost = direct costs + indirect costs + maintenance cost + opportunity cost
Thus, total cost = $[(92 + 4.2) + 12 + 40 + 5] \times 1000 = 153.2 \times 1000 = 1,53,200$ $ (**Ans.**)

Example 2.3.

In a proposed engineering project, the following elemental costs (in present value) are estimated (in US$):

Instrument cost = 25000
Instrument installation and training = 5000

Operation and maintenance cost for the effective life = 22000

Indirect costs = 20000

Opportunity cost of the land resource = 10000

Determine the real cost of the proposed project.

Solution:

We get

Total cost = direct costs + indirect costs + operation and maintenance cost + opportunity cost

Thus, total cost = [25000 +5000 + 22000 + 20000 + 10000] = 82,000 US$ (**Ans.**)

Example 2.4.

A Lathe machine was bought with US$5000 in 2000 and its value in 2012 (the end of effective life) is US$ 500. Find out:

a)   Depreciation amount

b)   Depreciation rate

Solution:

Given:

Initial (or first) cost, F = US$5000

Salvage value (at the end of effective life), S = US$ 500

Time span / effective life of the machine = 2012 – 2000 = 12 yrs

a)   Depreciation amount = initial cost – salvage value

= (5000 - 500) US$ = 4500 US$ (**Ans.**)

b)   We know, depreciation rate, $D_{SL} = \dfrac{F-S}{n}$

= 4500 /12 = 375 US$/yr (**Ans.**)

Example 2.5.

The first cost of an asset is US$95000, expected effective life is 15 years, and salvage value is expected to US$5000. Calculate:

a)   The depreciation rate

b)   Value of the asset after 10 years

Solution:

(i)   We know, depreciation rate, $D_{SL} = \dfrac{F-S}{n}$

Here

F = 95000
S = 5000
N = 15

Thus, $D_{SL} = \frac{95000-5000}{15} = 6000$ \$/yr **(Ans.)**

(ii)   Value of the asset after 10 years,

$$BV_t = F - \left(\frac{F-S}{n}\right) \times t = 95000 - 6000 \times 10 = 35000 \text{ \$ } \textbf{(Ans.)}$$

Example 2.6.

In an oil reserve, the estimated amount at the starting of withdrawal is 5×10^9 m^3. After 15 years of withdrawal, it lowered to 4×10^3 m^3. Calculate:

a) The depletion
b) The average depletion rate.

Solution:
Initial oil reserve = 50000000 m^3
Reserve after withdrawal = 4000 m^3
Duration of withdrawal = 15 yrs
a)   The depletion amount = (Initial reserve – Final reserve) = (50000000 – 4000) m^3
= 49996000 m^3 **(Ans.)**
b)   Average depletion rate = (Initial reserve – Final reserve)/ duration of depletion
=   depletion amount /duration
=   49996000 m^3 / 15 yrs
= 3333066.7 m^3/yr **(Ans.)**

Example 2.7.

In a main aquifer of 'North China Plain Area', the groundwater reserve (estimated) at the starting of pump irrigation was 7×10^8 m^3. After 10 years of irrigation, the amount came down to 6×10^6 m^3. What is the depletion rate of the aquifer reserve?

Solution:
Initial groundwater reserve = 7×10^8 m^3
      Reserve after withdrawal = 6×10^6 m^3
      Duration of withdrawal = 10 yrs
a)   The depletion amount =   (Initial reserve – Final reserve) =
      $(7 \times 10^8 - 6 \times 10^6)$ m^3
= 6.94 $\times 10^8$ m^3 **(Ans.)**

b)   Average depletion rate = depletion amount /duration

= 6.94×10^8 m^3 / 10 yrs

= 6.94×10^7 m^3/yr **(Ans.)**

Example 2.8.

The price of 'A basket of essential items (certain amount of each)' in 2010 was 500 US$, and the price of those items (of that basket, same amount) becomes 550 US$ in 2012. What is the inflation rate?

Solution:
Given:
Price in 2010 = 500 US$
Price in 2012 = 550 US$
Increase in price in 2 yrs = (550 – 500)US$ = 50 US$
Percent increase in price per year (i.e. inflation) =
= 100 [(increase in price)/year]/original price
 = 100 × [(50/2)/500] = 5
That is, inflation = 5 % **(Ans.)**

Example 2.9.

The 'Consumer Price Index (CPI)' of different years at Tokyo city is given below:

Year	Cost (US$)
2009	200
2010	205
2011	207
2012	210

Calculate:
a)   The inflation for each year
b)   Average inflation over the period

Solution:
Percent increase in price per year (i.e. inflation) =
=100 [(increase in price)/year]/original price

a)   Inflation in year incremental year:

Year	Increase in cost (US$)	Inflation rate (%)
2009-10	5	2.5
2010-11	2	0.98
2011-12	3	1.45

b)   Average inflation over the years = (2.5 + 0.98 + 1.45)/3 = 1.64 % (**Ans.**)

Example 2.10.

In Malaysia, the incremental tax rates on taxable income for the year 2010 are given below (Source: LHDN, Malaysia):

Income range (MYR)	Income amount/ fragmentation	Tax (MYR)	
		Based on rate (%)	Lump sum
0 – 2500	Up to 2500	0	0
2,501 – 5,000	2500	1	-
5,001 – 10,000	First 5,000	-	25
	Next 5,000	3	-
10,001 - 20,000	First 10,000	-	175
	Next 10,000	3	-
20,001 - 35,000	First 20,000	-	475
	Next 15,000	7	-
35,001 - 50,000	First 35,000	-	1525
	Next 15,000	12	-
50,001 - 70,000	First 50,000	-	3325
	Next 20,000	19	-
70,000 – 100,000	First 70,000	-	7175
	Next 30,000	24	-
Over 100,000	First 100,000	-	14325
	Next	26	-

MYR = Malaysian Ringgit.

Calculate the tax amount of '*Sunflower Oil Industry Limited*', whose income (net profit) is 50,500 MYR for that year.

Solution:
Given:
Income = 50,500 MYR
For the above income range, the tax rate is:

		Percent	Lump sum
50,001 - 70,000	First 50,000	-	3325
	Next 20,000	19	-

Total tax = 3325 + [50,500 – 50,000] × 19/100
= 3325 + 95 = 3420 MYR (**Ans.**)

Example 2.11.

Based on the 'incremental tax rate' mentioned in *Example 2.10*, calculate the tax amount of a businessman, whose taxable income is 25,000 MYR.

Solution:
Given:
Income = 25,000 MYR
For the above income range, the tax rate is:

		Percent	Lump sum
20,001 - 35,000	First 20,000	-	475
	Next 15,000	7	-

Total tax = 475 + (7/100) × [25,000 – 20,000]
= 475 + 350 = 825 MYR (**Ans.**)

Example 2.12.

To transfer 30 tons of building materials from its original position to 250 m apart, 3 options are available: *robot*, *mechanical*, and *manual*. The respective time required for each option and associated cost rate are as follows:

	Time required (hr)	Cost (RM)/hr
Robot	3	90
Mechanical	1.6	200
Manual	2	150

Which option will you suggest?

Soln
Here, the 'minimum' or 'least cost' option is the economic option. The total cost required by each option is as follows:

	Time required (hr)	Cost rate (RM/hr)	Total cost, RM (cost rate × time)
Robot	3	90	**270**
Mechanical	1.6	200	320
Manual	2	150	300

Among the options, the 'Robot' requires minimum or least cost. Hence, this option is suggested.

Example 2.13.

A dam has been proposed to build in a hilly area to supply water for agricultural purposes. The cost of construction (initial cost), if spread out to its effective life, becomes US$ 3000 per annum. The operating cost of the project is expected to US$ 2000 per annum, and the opportunity cost of the land resources used for dam construction is about US$ 500 per annum. The yearly water supply capacity of the dam is 5×10^4 m^3. The government has decided to operate the system as *"no profit – no loss"* principle. What would be the price of unit volume of water (1 m^3) to satisfy the above condition?

Soln
Calculation of yearly total cost

Yearly construction cost =   3000   US$
Yearly operating cost =   2000   ,
Yearly opportunity cost =   500   ,

Total yearly cost = (construction cost +   operating cost + opportunity cost)

= (3000 + 2000 + 500)
= 5500 US$

Calculation of yearly total revenue

From the given data, it is observed that the source of revenue of the project is the sale value of water.
Given
yearly supply of water =   50000 m^3

Let P is the price (in US$) of unit volume ($1$ m^3) of water

Thus, the total price of water (i.e. revenue) = $50000 \times P$ US$

Now, for the given condition, i.e. *"no profit - no loss"*, the yearly total cost must be equal to the yearly total revenue.

That is, $50000 \times P =$ 5500
or, P =   0.11

Thus, the price of 1 m^3 of water is   0.11   US$ (**Ans.**)
or, the price of water is   0.11   US$/$m^3$ (**Ans.**)

Example 2.14.

A private water-supply company "Aqua-link" has signed a contract with Province Government to supply purified drinking-water to a locality. The company agreed to supply water at 10% profit of the real cost, and the Govt. agreed to pay for if any purified water (of the rated capacity) not sold out. The cost of the infrastructure and set up of the instruments, if spread out to its effective life, becomes US$ 3,000 per annum. The annual operational and maintenance cost is approximated at US$ 20,000 per annum. The supply capacity of the system is 120 m^3 per day. According to the stated contract, what would be the price of unit volume (1 m^3) of purified water?

Soln

Infrastructural cost/yr	= 4000 US$	
Operation and maintenance cost/yr	= 25000 US$	

Total cost/yr =	(4000 + 25000)	= 29000 US$
Taking 10% profit, total sale value		= 31900 US$/yr

Production *or* output =	120	m^3/d
=	43800	m^3/yr

Cost/m^3 of water = (total cost / total production) = (31900 US$/yr / 43800 m^3/yr)
$$= 0.73 \text{ US\$}$$
That is, cost of unit volume (1 m^3) of water = 0.73 US$ (**Ans.**)

Example 2.15.

The "IRCON Construction Ltd." has got a highway construction work from Dhaka to Chittagong (in Bangladesh). There are two sites/options to set up 'construction haul'. The 'temporary building/facility development cost' for both the sites is similar. Other relevant information and cost items of the sites are given below:

	Description/cost items	Site 1	Site 2
1	Lease value/rental of the land for the work period ($)	8000	9000
2	Average travel distance of the spot from the *haul* (for carrying the construction materials) (Km)	3.5	2.7
3	Estimated total materials to be carried (ton)	2000	
4	Carrying (Fuel) cost of the materials to the spot ($/t/km)	7	6

Which site should the construction company choose?

Soln

The variable costs for both the sites are summarized below:

Variable cost items	Site 1	Site 2
Lease *or* rental cost, $	8000	9000
Total fuel/carrying cost, $ (total material × distance × rate)	49000	32400
Total variable cost	57000	41400

The "site-2" needs minimum *or* least cost, hence this site should be chosen. (**Ans.**)

Example 2.16.

The annualized value of initial cost, yearly running cost, and the product per year of 3 different machines are given below:

	Annualized initial cost (US$/yr)	Running cost (US$/yr)	Number of product/year
Machine-1	1200	550	8000
Machine-2	1400	520	8300
Machine-3	1600	480	8500

Find out the *least cost* machine.

Soln

The Machine under which the cost of unit production is lowest, is the *least cost* machine. The calculation is summarized below:

	Annualized initial cost (US$/yr)	Running cost (US$/yr)	Total cost per year (US$)	Number of product/year	Cost per product ($)
Machine-1	1200	550	1750	8000	**0.22**
Machine-2	1400	520	1920	8300	0.23
Machine-3	1600	480	2080	8500	0.24

"Machine-1" is the *least cost* machine. (**Ans.**)

Example 2.17.

A 'Palm Oil Refining Industry' has 3 options/techniques to purify the crude oil. The initial cost of the equipments under each technique, operating cost (both are expressed in equivalent annual basis), and the capacity of each option is given as follows:

	Initial cost ($/yr)	Operating cost ($/yr)	Capacity (gallon/day)
1	4,000	90000	200
2	3,500	87500	180
3	2,700	98000	150

Economic life of the equipments under each technique is similar. Which option do you suggest?

Soln

The option which will give 'least cost' per unit of product (purified oil), is the most economic.

The analysis is summarized below:

Option	Initial cost ($/yr)	Operating cost ($/yr)	Capacity (gallon/day)	Yearly capacity (gallon/yr)	Total cost ($/yr)	cost/ gallon($)
1	4,000	90000	200	73000	94,000	**1.288**
2	3,500	87500	180	65700	91,000	1.385
3	2,700	98000	150	54750	100,700	1.839

The option-1 gives '*least cost*' to purify 01 gallon of oil, thus this option is suggested. (**Ans.**)

Example 2.18.

A manufacturing company is planning to buy a machine to produce 'spare parts' of the Bi-cycle. Three options/machines are available. The cost and production efficiency of the machines are given below. The economic life of the machines and the quality of the products are similar.

	Annualized value of initial cost ($)	Total product (spare parts) per month (nos)	Defective product per month (% of total)	Annualized value of operating and maintenance cost ($)
Machine -1	21000	875	3	46000
Machine-2	21500	900	3.5	55000
Machine-3	20500	870	2.5	52000

Suggest the best machine.

Soln

Yearly total cost = capital cost ($/yr) + operational cost ($/yr)
Yearly total product = monthly product × 12
Yearly defective product = percent of defective product × yearly total product
Yearly good product = total product − defective product

Cost per good product = total cost / number of good product

The calculation is summarized below:

	Yearly total cost ($)	Yearly total product (spare parts) (nos)	Yearly defective product (nos)	Yearly good product (nos)	Cost per good product ($)
Machine-1	67000	10500	315	10185	**6.58**
Machine-2	76500	10800	378	10422	7.34
Machine-3	72500	10440	261	10179	7.12

From analysis it is seen that **Machine-1** is the *least cost Machine*, hence it is most economical. Thereby, it is suggested to buy.

Example 2.19.

A business firm is considering to set up a "Ready-made Garment Factory" to a low labor-cost country in Asia. Suppose, you are the Chief of firm's engineering department and you have been given the job to evaluate various alternatives.

In the industry (also termed as 'Factory'), 2000 machines will be in operation, and that will require 2000 operators. The initial/first cost is the same for all options. Other variable cost elements of various options are given below.

Assume that the quality of the product, and also the price, will be same for all origins. Which option will you suggest?

Variable cost in different countries:

Country	Operating cost other than the machine operator	Wage of unit operator (US$/month)	Finished cloth per operator per month (nos)	Transportation cost to carry the product at target location
India	12000	200	200	15000
Bangladesh	12000	190	210	14000
Pakistan	12500	210	205	15500
China	15000	220	220	16000
Indonesia	13000	188	205	13500

Soln

'Total variable cost' per unit of product is the *least cost* (economic) option.
Before calculation, all data are converted to yearly value.
The calculations are summarized below:

Country	Wage of operators (US$/yr)	Operating cost (US$/yr)	Transportation cost (US$/yr)	Total cost (US$/yr)	Total finished cloth per year (nos)	Variable cost per finished cloth (US$/cloth)
India	400000	12000	15000	427000	400000	1.068
Bangladesh	380000	12000	14000	406000	420000	**0.967**
Pakistan	420000	12500	15500	448000	410000	1.093
China	440000	15000	16000	471000	440000	1.070
Indonesia	376000	13000	13500	402500	410000	0.982

The option-2 (Bangladesh) shows *least cost*. Hence, this country is suggested. (**Ans.**)

Example 2.20.

At the Mid Valley area in USA, the estimated cost of an irrigation project, expressed as annual value, is US$ 10,000 (at the beginning of the project). The yearly value (annualized) of the operation and maintenance cost is 15% of the initial cost. The annual benefit from the project is estimated at US$ 12,000. The effective life of the project is expected to 30 years. Do you think that the project is economically viable? Assume no salvage value at the end of project.

Soln
Annual capital cost = 10000 US$
Annual operation and maintenance cost = 15% of initial
= (15/100) ×10000 = 1500 US$

Total annual cost, C = capital cost + ope. and maintenance cost = 11500 US$

Given,
Total annual benefit, B = 12000   US$

Thus, BCR = B/C = 1.04

As the BCR>1.0, the project is economically justified. (**Ans.**)

Example 2.21.

In a water-logged problem area of Pakistan, 120 ha land has the potential for crop production. The Province Government wishes to set up a drainage system to regain the productivity of the land. As an engineer, you are asked to advise regarding the technical and economic feasibility of the proposed drainage project. From the preliminary study of the area, the following information are gathered:

Initial total cost of installation, expressed in yearly basis = US$ 15,000

Yearly operational cost (collection and disposal of drainage outflow,
maintenance, others, including salary of the technical staff) = US$ 30,000

Economic life of the installed system = 20 yrs

Tentative yearly revenue to be generated from the crop production =
= US$ 60,000
Do you think that the drainage project is economically viable?

Soln

Yearly capital cost = 15000 US$

Yearly operational cost = 30000 US$

Yearly total cost = (15000 + 30000) = 45000 US$

Yearly revenue = 60000 US$

BCR = yearly benefit / yearly cost = 60000/45000 = 1.3

Since BCR >1.0, the project is economically justified. (**Ans.**)

Exercise

2.1 Explain the following curves with sketch:
     Demand curve, supply curve, cost curve, revenue curve
2.2 Explain the behaviour of supply and demand curve.
2.3 Narrate the characteristics and behaviours of cost and revenue curve.
2.4 Explain why the 'demand curve' moves downward and 'supply curve' moves
upward.
2.5 What are the categories and components of cost of engineering works? Discuss.
2.6 (a) What is effective life of an asset?
     (b) Mention the effective life of the following structures:
RCC road, asphalt/bituminous road, bridge, brick/cement concrete canal, RCC building
2.7 (a) What is depreciation?
     (b) Discuss the procedure of calculating book and tax depreciation.
2.8 Explain the following terms: Opportunity cost, BCR, Depletion
2.9 Discuss the factors affecting value of money.
2.10 Explain the elements of cost of 06 engineering works
2.11 Explain the following terms (with calculation procedure, where applicable):
     Cost and revenue function, economic growth rate, GDP, GNP
2.12 (a) Explain the terms 'inflation' and 'deflation'.
     (b) Explain the impact of deflation on national economy
     (c) Explain why too much inflation is bad for economy

2.13 Cost of production for 4 ton wheat in one hectare land is US$300, and it is US$550 for 6 ton. What is the marginal cost of production?

2.14 Cost of production for 5 ton Maize in one hectare land is US$450, and it is US$550 for 6 ton. What is the marginal cost of production of maize?

2.15 The first cost of an asset is US$98000, expected effective life is 16 years, and salvage value is expected to US$6000. Calculate:
i)   The depreciation rate
ii) Value of the asset after 12 years

2.16 The initial cost of an asset is US$88500, expected effective life is 10 years, and salvage value is expected to US$4000. Calculate the value of the asset after 7 years.

2.17 In a proposed engineering project, the following elemental costs are estimated (in million dollar):
Instrument cost = 1.0
Instrument installation and training = 0.2
Operation and maintenance cost for the effective life = 0.7
Indirect costs = 0.3
Opportunity cost of the land resource = 0.1

Determine the cost of the proposed project.

2.18 An engineering project is proposed to implement. The following elemental costs are estimated ('000 $):
Instrument cost = 92
Instrument installation and training = 4.2
Indirect costs = 12
Operation and maintenance cost for the effective life = 40
Opportunity cost of the land resource = 5

Determine the total cost of the proposed project.

2.19 In an oil reserve at hilly tract area, the estimated amount at the starting of withdrawal was 7×10^7 m^3. After 10 years of withdrawal, it lowered to 6.4×10^4 m^3. Calculate:

(a) The depletion amount
(b) The average depletion rate

2.20 In a main aquifer of 'Murray Darling Basin Area', the groundwater reserve (estimated) at the starting of pump irrigation was 7×10^8 m^3. After 10 years of irrigation, the amount came down to 6×10^6 m^3. What is the depletion rate of the aquifer reserve?

2.21 The price of 'A basket of essential items (certain amount of each)' in 2011 was 600 US$, and the price of those items (of that basket, same amount) becomes 630 US$ in 2012. What is the inflation rate?

2.22 The 'Consumer Price Index (CPI)' of different years at Melbourne City is given below:

Year	Cost (US$)
2010	305
2011	315
2012	328

Calculate:
a) The inflation for each year
b) Average inflation over the period

2.23 A dam has been proposed to build in a seasonally-dry area to supply water for agricultural purposes. The cost of construction (initial cost), if spread out to its effective life, becomes US$ 5000 per annum. The operating cost of the project is expected to US$ 2300 per annum, and the opportunity cost of the land resources used for dam construction is about US$ 600 per annum. The yearly water supply capacity of the dam is 6×10^5 m^3. The government has decided to operate the system as *"no profit – no loss"* principle. What would be the price of unit volume of water to satisfy the above condition?

2.24 The "CONTRA Construction Ltd." has got a highway construction work from Kuala Lumpur to Pahang (in Malaysia). There are two sites/options to set up 'construction haul'. The 'temporary building/facility development cost' for both the sites is similar. Other relevant information and cost items of the sites are given below:

	Description /cost items	Site-1	Site-2
1	Lease value/rental of the land for the work period ($)	2000	5000
2	Average travel distance of the spot from the *haul* (for carrying the construction materials) (Km)	3.1	1.7
3	Estimated total materials to be carried (ton)	3000	
4	Carrying (Fuel) cost of the materials to the spot ($/t/km)	4.2	5.1

Which site should the construction company choose?

2.25 The annualized value of initial cost, yearly running cost, and the product per year of 3 different machines are given below:

	Annualized initial cost (US$/yr)	Running cost (US$/yr)	Number of product/year
Machine-1	1500	350	6000
Machine-2	1200	420	6300
Machine-3	1300	480	4500

Find out the *least cost* machine.

2.26   A 'Cruid Oil Refining Industry' has 3 options/techniques to purify the crude oil. The initial cost of the equipments under each technique, operating cost (both are expressed in equivalent annual basis), and the capacity of each option is given below:

	Initial cost ($/yr)	Operating cost ($/yr)	Capacity (gallon/day)
1	3,500	37000	200
2	3,000	44500	180
3	3,700	78000	250

Economic life of the equipments under each technique is similar. Which option do you suggest?

2.27   A manufacturing company is planning to buy a machine to produce 'spare parts' of the Car. Four options/machines are available. The cost and production efficiency of the machines are given below. The economic life of the machines and the quality of the products are similar.

	Annualized value of initial cost ($)	Total product (spare parts) per month (nos)	Defective product per month (% of total)	Annualized value of operating and maintenance cost ($)
Machine -1	31000	575	2.7	41000
Machine-2	23500	600	3.5	51000
Machine-3	25500	770	2.5	52000
Machine-4	26500	790	2.7	56000

Suggest the best machine.

2.28   A business firm is considering to set up a "Ready-made Garment Factory" to a low labor-cost country in Asia. Suppose, you are the Chief of firm's engineering department and you have been given the job to evaluate various alternatives. In the industry (also termed as 'Factory'), 1500 machines will be in operation, and that will require 1500 operators. The initial/first cost is the same for all options. Other variable cost elements of various options are given below. Assume that the quality of the product, and also the price, will be same for all origins. Which option will you suggest?

Variable costs in different countries:

Country	Operating cost other than the machine operator (US$/month)	Wage of unit operator (US$/month)	Finished cloth per operator per month (nos)	Transportation cost to carry the product at target location (US$/month)
China	10000	210	210	14000
Vietnam	9000	195	215	14000
Indonesia	90500	215	210	13500
India	11000	225	212	14000
Singapur	13000	250	225	14500

2.29   At the Muda Valley area in Malaysia, the estimated cost of an irrigation project, expressed as annual value, is US$ 12,000 (at the beginning of the project). The yearly value (annualized) of the operation and maintenance cost is 12% of the initial cost. The annual benefit from the project is estimated at US$ 14,000. The effective life of the project is expected to 20 years. Do you think that the project is economically viable? Assume no salvage value at the end of project.

2.30   In a water-logged problem area at Melbourne, Australia, 230 ha land has the potential for crop production. The State Government wishes to set up a drainage system to regain the productivity of the land. As an engineer, you are asked to advise regarding the technical and economic feasibility of the proposed drainage project. From the preliminary study of the area, the following information are gathered:

Initial total cost of installation, expressed in yearly basis = US$ 12,000

Yearly operational cost (collection and disposal of drainage outflow, maintenance, others, including salary of the technical staff) = US$ 32,000

Economic life of the installed system = 15 yrs

Tentative yearly revenue to be generated from the crop production
= US$ 56,000

Do you think that the drainage project is economically viable?

Chapter 3

DATA SOURCES, DEMAND FORECASTING, AND COST ESTIMATION FOR PROJECT ANALYSIS

3.1. TYPES OF DATA REQUIRED

3.1.1. Background and Need

Proper preparation of an economic analysis requires a major effort to gather data, do mathematical calculations, and summarize results into required report formats. Use of currently available computer programs can reduce the time required, ensure correct calculations, and produce results. *A word of caution*: results from computer runs are only as good as the data input, so valid data must be used. The most challenging aspect of economic analysis is identifying the benefits and costs and their quantification.

Accurately forecasting the cost and outcome/benefit of future projects is vital for its success. The first step in financial and economic analysis of engineering development project is to identify appropriate data and to understand their potentials and their limitations.

This chapter provides an overview of the data needs for economic analysis, considering how data requirements may vary depending on the analytical issues at hand. The chapter also provides a brief guide to different sources of data and their respective limitations. Although there is some scope for using routine data, such as administrative records or census data, recent survey data tend to have the greatest potential for assessing and analyzing different aspects of project.

3.1.2. Types of Sectors of Analysis

A: Industry
(i)   Aerospace,
(ii) Agricultural chemicals,
(iii) Agricultural crop production,
(iv) Agricultural stock production,
(v)   Coal mining, and
(vi) Oil and gas exploration and production.

B: structural
(a) Highway
(b) Bridge
(c) Building/housing
(d) Dam
(e) Barrage

C: power generation
i.   Hydro-electric power plant
ii.   Renewable energy farm (solar, wind, wave, geo-thermal, etc.)
iii. Thermal power plant

Within a specific type of work, there may have different options (technological/material combination) to perform the same job. Economic analysis should be performed for each case also.

3.1.3. Types of Data Required

The following types of data may be required in analyzing engineering project:

- Engineering data
- Management data
- Support data / relevant data
- Other complementary data

You have to gauge/estimate how much management section will be (e.g. technical, general administration, finance, maintenance /support service, etc.) and how much manpower will be required in each section to operate the system smoothly.

Support/relevant data include transportation facility and distance from town/port, on which cost of import/export will depend.

Other complementary data – such as socio-economic condition of the locality; if the project is labor intensive, then required manpower will be available or not. If the local manpower is scarce (or become competitive), operation cost may be increased.

3.2. DEMAND FORECASTING AND DETERMINATION OF DESIGN CAPACITY

3.2.1. Demand Forecasting

As the projects are planned to solve a problem *or* to satisfy the required demand, accurate forecasting/projection of the required demand (e.g. traffic load, electricity demand, water demand, etc. for a community *or* town) is essential. Demand forecasting requires the following points to consider:

- Planning period (e.g. 50 yrs or 100 yrs projection)
- Population growth / urbanization rate
- Change in income
- Change in habit

Demand should be forecasted with appropriate method/technique/model considering the above points.

Population can be forecasted using the following formula:

$$F_{pn} = P_p(1 + \frac{g_r}{100})^n. \tag{3.1}$$

where

F_{pn} = forecasted population [nos] at year n from now (n = future target year – present year)

P_p = present population (nos)

g_r = expected average population growth rate during this period (%)

3.2.2. Supply Forecasting and Design Capacity Estimation

In case of natural resources project, specially water resources project, you have to analyze 'low flow' or 'minimum availability', and also have to consider change in environment/climate over time, and consequently change in natural flow pattern. For example, in case of designing water reservoir, you have to calculate reservoir capacity based on lowest probable rainfall (normally considered as 'rainfall at 80% probability of exceedence')- to ensure fulfilling demand during low-rainfall year(s). In contrast, height of embankment *or* retaining wall should be based on the probable highest rainfall/flood – to ensure protection during high rainfall or flood year(s).

3.2.3. Workout Problems

Example 3.1.

Total population in an area in 2010 is 1.7 million. What would be the population in that area in 2030, if the average population growth rate in the area during this period is 1.5%?

Soln

We get, future population,

$$F_{pn} = P_p(1 + \frac{g_r}{100})^n$$

Given:

Present population, P_p = 1.7 million

Population growth rate, gr = 1.5 %

Time period, n = 2030 – 2010 = 20 yrs

Putting the values, $F_{pn} = 1.7 \times \left(1 + \frac{1.5}{100}\right)^{20} = 2.2897$ million (**Ans.**)

Example 3.2.

A new 'Food and Beverage' Industry at Tokyo City is planning to set up its production capacity based on local demand. After a survey of market demand, it is found that the present (year 2012) demand per day is 500 items. The company is targeting its capacity 10 years ahead (that is, to capable of satisfying the demand in year 2022). It is expected that due to increase in population, the demand will increase by 20% of the present in year 2022.

What should be the design production capacity of the industry in accordance with the above condition?

Soln

Present demand = 500 items/d
Increase in demand due to increase in population = 500 × 20% = 100 items
Thus, total daily demand at year 2022 = 500 + 100 = 600 items

Assuming that the Industry will be in operation 7 days a week, design production capacity of the industry should be 600 items/d   (**Ans.**)
If the Industry operates 5 days a week, then the design production capacity should be (600×7)/5 = 840 items/d (**Ans**)

Example 3.3.

In a new proposed town at Pahang, Malaysia, the present design population is 1500 and daily per capita water demand is projected to 150 liter. As an Executive Engineer of that locality, you are going to design water-supply project. You are planning the water supply capacity for 30 years projection. Expected average population increase during this period is 5% per annum, and the increase in per capita water-demand due to change in income during the projected period is expected to 8%.

(a) Determine the design capacity of the water-supply project.
(b) What is the per capita water demand at the end of projection year?

Soln

(**a**) Given:
Present population = 1500 nos
Demand per person = 150 liter
Total present demand = 1500 × 150 = 225000 liter   (i)
Design period =   30 yrs
Population growth rate =   5 %
Total population at the end of projection yr (year 30) =
= 1500 ×(1+ 5/100)^{30} = 6483 nos
Increase in population =   6483 − 1500 = 4983
Demand for the additional population = 4983 × 150
= 747437 liter   (ii)
Increase in demand due to change in income = 8 %

Demand for income change (for the whole population) =

= 6483 × (150 × 8/100)

= 77795 liter   (iii)

    Total demand (i.e. design demand) = (i) + (ii) + (iii)

= 1050232 liter (**Ans.**)

(b) Per capital demand = total demand / total population

= 1050232 liter / 6483

= 162.0 liter (**Ans.**)

Example 3.4.

In a new resort city at Kuantan, Malaysia, the present population is 1000 and daily per capita water demand (normal demand) is 150 liter (including household, gardening, car washing, etc.). But there is a deficit of water by 10% of the demand. As an Executive Engineer of the City Corporation, you are going to submit a water-supply project to the higher authority. For that purpose, you will perform economic analysis of different supply options for the projected demand. You are planning the project for 20 yrs projection. Expected average population increase (growth rate) during this period is 2% per annum, and the increase in per capita water-demand due to change in income is expected to 10% (during 20 yrs period, not annually). Determine the design capacity of the water-supply project.

Soln

For the given condition, we get:

Design capacity = present deficit + normal demand for the increased (new) people + extra demand due to change in income for the total people.

Given:

Present population, P = 1000

Present demand =150 lit/capita

Shortage = 10%

Total shortage =1000 × (150 × 10/100) = 15000 lit   (i)

Population growth rate =2%

Projection period, n = 20 yrs

Future population, $F_{pn} = 1000 \times \left(1 + \frac{2}{100}\right)^{20} = 1485.95 \approx 1486$

Extra /new population =   1486 – 1000 = 486

Normal demand for new people = 486 × 150 = 72892.1 lit   (ii)

Demand due to income change (for the whole people) = 10% of normal demand

= 10% × (150 ×1486)

= 22289   lit   (iii)

Design capacity = (i) + (ii) + (iii) = 110181 lit/day (**Ans.**)

Example 3.5.

A 'Social Marketing Company' is planning to set up an industry at New York city to produce 'Cosmetic items'. The company is planning to fix its production capacity based on local demand (New York only). After a survey of market demand, it is found that the present (year 2012) demand per day is 3000 items. The company is targeting its capacity 15 years ahead (i.e. to capable of satisfying the demand in year 2027). It is expected that due to increase in population, the demand will increase by 20% of the present in year 2025; and also due to change in habit as a result of increase in per capita income, demand will increase by 10%. What would be the design 'production capacity' of the industry?

> **Soln**
> Present demand = 3000   item/day   (i)
> Present year =2012, Future yr = 2027
> Time period (yr) for increase =15
> Increase in demand due to increase in population = 20 % of the present
> = 3000 × (20/100)
> = 600 item/d   (ii)
> Increase in demand due to change in habit as a result of change in income
> = 10% of the present
> = 3000 × (10/100)
> = 300 item/d   (iii)
> Total demand in 2025 = (i) + (ii) + (iii) = 3000 + 600 + 300 = 3900 item/d
> Assuming that the industry will be in operation 7 days a week,
> the design capacity (Q) of the industry would be 3900 items/day(**Ans.**).
> If the industry operates 6 days in a week, then the design capacity should be (to satisfy

the weekly demand)

(Q x 7)/6 = 4550 items/day (**Ans.**).

If the industry operates 5 days in a week, then the design capacity should be (Q x 7)/5 = 5460 items/day (**Ans.**).

3.3. DATA SOURCES

3.3.1. Relevant Publications

Statistical Yearbook

Yearly publication of '*National Bureau of Statistics*' contains data of various types including quantification of natural resources, incomes, population, national economic indices, etc.

Censuses

Censuses (publication of the '*Bureau of the Census*') are an important source of data for planning and monitoring of population issues and socioeconomic and environmental trends, in both developed and developing countries. National population and housing censuses also provide valuable statistics and indicators for assessing the situation of various special population groups, such as those affected by gender issues, children, youth, the elderly, persons with a disability, and the migrant population.

3.3.2. Relevant Departments

Relevant departments for different types of data are given below.

Table 3.1. Data types and relevant departments for data availability

Sl no.	Type of work	Type of data	Source Department
1	Water Engg. works (Dam, Barrage,etc.)	Rainfall, flood	Department of Meteorology Water Development Board
2	Roads, Highway	Land map, price of land	Department of Land Resources
		Traffic load/density	Department of Roads and Highway Metropolitan city / City Corporation Department of Transportation
3	Building	Price of building materials	Public Works Department Relevant industry / industry trade association Relevant govt. Agencies/Departments
		Price index	Statistical Yearbook
		Price of land	Department of Land Resources
4	Chemical industry		
5	Cement industry		
6	Steel industry		
7	Agro-based industry	Availability of the agro-product, their prices	Statistical Year-book, Department of Agriculture
		Price of the equipments	Relevant industries and their book-let
8	Renewable energy plant	Availability of renewable energy	Department of Energy
		Price of elements	Statistical Year-book, Relevant industries and their book-let

3.3.3. Where No Data Is Available

The use of expert opinion (or discussion with engineers) is appropriate in situations in which there is little or no published material in a particular area, or in which the results of a thorough literature review or meta-analysis are considered unreliable, conflicting, or insufficient to cover the requirements of a study. Investigation through internet search may also be useful.

3.3.4. Economic Analysis at the Global Level

The engineering farm may bid for international project, and for that, international data may be required. Publications of 'World Bank', FAO, WTO, WMO, and other international organizations may be useful. Data of a specific country may be collected from the publication of that country.

3.3.5. Limitations of Data Sources

Limitations of different sources of data are given below (Table 3.2):

Table 3.2. Advantages and limitations of different source data

Type of data	Advantage	Disadvantage/ Limitation
Market survey data	Data are representative for a specific location and current time/rate	Time consuming and troublesome
Administrative data	Data are readily available	Data may not be representative for all cases
Census data	Data are readily available	Limited data may be available

3.3.6. Data Checking

The analyst should review the data for accuracy and adequacy, and report any major questions, data gaps, or other deficiencies to the work group to address possible shortcomings before analysis. The economic analyst should then supplement these collected data with available primary and secondary sources to complete the data profile.

3.4. COST ESTIMATION

3.4.1. Concepts and Terminologies

Cost estimation is one of the most important parts of economic analysis for all types of project. It is needed at different stages of the projects. A cost estimate at a given stage of the project development represents the prediction of cost based on the available data. The Engineers should apply their judgment and experience in the application of scientific principles and techniques to estimate cost, cost control, and profitability. One of the most challenging aspect of economic analysis is identifying those benefits and costs that resist quantification. These typically include aesthetics, safety, environmental impact, historic preservation.

Before discussing the cost estimation issues and guidelines, some relevant definitions are discussed below.

Project

Projects cover any work from 'a short period engineering effort to solve a problem' to 'large as billion dollars investment work, for example, constructing tunnel below the sea bed from one country to another'. Engineering and industrial projects are familiar to all, examples are: constructing a bridge, building, super market, highway, airport, power generation plant (hydro, oil or nuclear), chemical industry, manufacturing industry, garment factory/industry, process plants industry (water purification, wastewater treatment, etc.), etc.

Recurring Cost

Recurring cost is the cost that recurs *or* repeats time to time (i.e. repeating specific time interval) during the life span of an investment scheme or project.

Annuity

A series of equal payments at equal time intervals.

Redundancy

Existence of more than one way *or* means to perform a specific function or task.

Contingency

It is the provision for uncertainties. In most large projects, there is an allowance for contingencies *or* uncertainty *or* unexpected costs occurring during construction and/or implementation stage.

3.4.2. Stages of Cost Estimation

Cost estimations are preform at various stages of a project:

- Initial guess estimate
- Preliminary estimate
- Final estimate

(a) Initial guess estimate

This type of estimate is done at the very beginning (conceptual stage) of the project. It is normally done based on the record of past similar projects, but adjustment is made for new capacity, price escalation, etc.

(b) Preliminary estimate

After the completion of conceptual design of the project, listing the category and size of the required machine/equipments, and completion of overall process flow diagram, this estimate is prepared. At this stage, total direct cost of the project is derived through quotations or in-house information (equipment, bulk material cost, labor man-hours and costs). Total indirect cost is estimated by a percentage of direct cost. Installation of materials and labor costs are estimated from ratios based on past project of similar type. Total cost is calculated adding cost for land, site development, building, supervision, start-up, and any adjustment if needed.

(c) Final estimate *or* detail estimate

This estimate is done after completion of process design and detail design. The basis of this estimate includes:

- Engineering costs
- Material costs

- Subcontract costs (if any) (based on lump sum *or* firm bids)
- Labor cost (based on detail man-hours and actual/local labor rate)
- Indirect costs

3.4.3. Cost Estimation Approaches

Numerous approaches are available to estimate the cost of a project. Based on the availability of information/data, estimating resources (software and hardware) and the purpose/stage of estimate, an appropriate approach (or a combination) can be chosen. The approaches include:

- Analogy approach
- Trend analysis
- Use of cost equation/function (parametric approach)
- Cost review and update approach
- Bottom up approach
- Consultation with relevant experts (expert opinion approach)

3.4.3.1. Analogy Approach
This approach relies on the cost of a similar item/instrument (which is known) bought in the past, or on the cost of similar project implemented in the past. Adjustments are made for the up scaling of price, governmental tax/tariff imposed, or increase in transportation cost.

3.4.3.2. Trend Analysis
Cost of similar item/instrument/project bought *or* implemented several times in the past are used to make projection/forecast for present *or* in near future time. At least 03 data points are needed to analyze/draw the trend. It is the extrapolation of past trend for the proposed/target time (Figure 3.1). The trend equation can also be used to estimate the present *or* future cost.

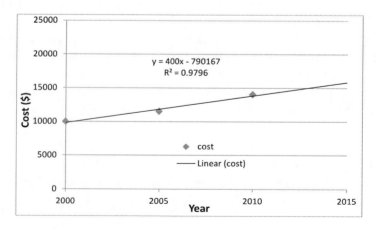

Figure 3.1. Trend graph of cost.

For example, the trend equation of total cost to set up a chemical industry is:

$$C = 1500 + 1.2\, Y \tag{3.2}$$

where

C = total construction cost, US$

Y = year of accomplishment.

3.4.3.3. Parametric Approach

In this approach, mathematical relationship is established between the total cost and cost drivers and/or other system parameters from historical data bases of similar projects (or industries). Relationship can be established similar to modeling approach - statistical correlation study, and regression analysis of the relevant parameters/factors with the cost. The resulting cost equation (or cost function) is used to estimate cost of new/proposed project.

The mathematical cost model can be of single relationship (equation) or model, or combination of several sub-components (or sub-models). This type of relationship/model can range from simple equation to more complex model.

Very often, a single parameter is used to describe a cost function. For example, the cost of a building is expressed as a function of cost per square feet of the floor area; the cost of a power plant (hydro- or fuel) is expressed as a function electricity generating capacity (megawatts); the cost of an oil refinery is expressed as a function of refining capacity per day (gallon per day); the cost of a sewerage treatment plant is expressed as a function of waste treated per day (hundred, thousand *or* million gallon per day); etc. Example of a building cost is:

$$C = 200 \times P \tag{3.3}$$

where

C = total construction cost, US$

P = area (floor *or* outer) of the building, ft^2 (or m^2)

The total cost derived using 'cost function' *should be adjusted* for the following aspects:

- Local index for construction cost
- Inflation rate
- Any regulatory change/constraint (e.g. imposing tax, tariff)

Local index for construction cost

The location where the construction has been accomplished, may be different from the location where the new construction to be furnished – which may be in terms of distance from the source of raw material (e.g. transportation cost), rate of labor, etc. This index is normally as multiplicative form. If the overall price for the new/target location is 3 percent higher than the previous location, the index is 1.03; if the price is 3 percent lower, the index is 0.97.

Inflation rate

The cost adjusted with local index, does not include the inflation *or* time value of money (escalation of price) *or* change in exchange rate of foreign currency (dollar). So the cost should be adjusted for the inflation rate. This can be accomplished using the formula:

$$C_{ad(i)} = C \times (1 + \frac{I_f}{100})^N \qquad\qquad (3.4)$$

where

$C_{ad(i)}$ = adjusted cost for inflation

C = earlier cost (adjusted for local cost index)

n = time period (number of years) between the time of *past data* (used for deriving cost function) and the target construction time

I_f = average inflation rate over the period (%)

Regulatory change/constraint

It includes the imposition of new/higher tax, tariff, etc.

3.4.3.4. Bottom up Approach

In this approach, required material quantities for a component of the project are estimated from the detail design / work statement / drawings and specifications. Then the cost of that component is calculated by multiplying the quantities with the present price (or past price in the absence of present price/cost). Total cost of the project is the summation of all the components. Adjustment of the cost is needed if the previous price/cost of the materials is used.

Mathematically it can be expressed as:

$$C_T = \Sigma_1(q_i \times p_i) + \Sigma_2(q_i \times p_i) + \cdots + \Sigma_n(q_i \times p_i) \qquad (3.5)$$

where 1, 2, 3, …..*n* are the components; q is the quantity, and p is the price.

3.4.3.5. Expert Opinion Approach

When sufficient data are not available, *or* in case of a brand new project where no past experience is available, *or* in case of a project for which available cost estimation methods do not match, consultation with relevant experts (specialist in the respective/relevant fields) is the alternative choice. Discussion and consultation should be repeated until a consensus of the cost estimation is reached.

It should be kept in mind that, the cost need to be adjusted for time scale (escalation due to 'time value of money', inflation), geographic location (transportation cost and variation of labor cost, etc.), regulatory change (imposition of tax, change in license fee, etc.), and variation of foreign currency rate (in case of importable items).

Based on the above approaches, numerous methods have been proposed to estimate cost (both for preliminary and final estimation) of a project.

3.4.4. Approximate Cost Estimation or Initial Cost Estimation

Many methods have been proposed to estimate guess *or* initial *or* approximate cost from past *or* present real cost of engineering or industrial projects. Some of them are discussed below.

Methods of approximate cost estimation include:

- Cost-capacity relation
- Lang factor method (for process plant)
- Hand method
- Wessel method
- Turnover ratio method

(i) Cost-capacity relationship

This method is used to estimate cost from similar recent project, plant, or equipment of different sizes or capacities. It is useful to get quick cost estimation with reasonable accuracy. The cost-capacity relationship is expressed as:

$$C_n = C_0 \left[\frac{K_n}{K_0}\right]^{\alpha} \qquad (3.6)$$

where C_n = cost of new project
C_0 = cost of past (or recent) similar project
K_n = capacity of the new project
K_0 = capacity of the past project
α = cost-capacity factor

The value of α can vary from 0.6 to 0.8.

(ii) Lang factor method

This method is first proposed by Lang (1947). In this method, total 'Plant Cost' is estimated from the delivered equipment cost. It is a method of obtaining quick order-of-magnitude cost utilizing historical average cost factor. Total plant cost is obtained as follows:

$$TPC = n \times DEC \qquad (3.7)$$

where,   TPC = estimated Total Plant Cost
n = Lang factor
DEC = Delivered Equipment Cost

Lang (1947) suggested n =3.1 for solid process plant, n= 3.63 for solid-fluid plant, and n= 4.74 for fluid process plant. For other types of plant/equipment, the value of *n* can be determined from past/historical cost data of similar plants/equipments.

(iii) Hand method

This method is suggested by W. E. Hand (1958). This is a form of revision of Lang (1947) method. In this revision, Hang proposed different factors for various groups of Plant or Equipment. The total cost of installment for a Plant or Equipment is given by:

$$TCI = m \times DEC \tag{3.8}$$

where,   TCI = total installment cost of a plant or equipment
         m = Hand factor
         DEC= delivered equipment cost

The Hang factor (m) covers the field materials, labor, and indirect costs. It does not cover contingency allowance. The suggested values of *m* are: for pumps, m = 4; for compressors, m = 2.5; for instruments, m = 4; for pressure vessel, m = 4; for heat exchangers, m = 2; for fractioning towers, m = 4; and for miscellaneous equipment, m = 2.5.

(iv) Wessel method

This method is used to estimate operating labour requirement. The estimation equation is expressed as (Humphreys, 1984):

$$\frac{OH}{\lambda} = \alpha \left[\frac{K}{P^{0.76}} \right] \tag{3.9}$$

where,   OH = number of operating man-hours
         λ = product in ton
         K = number of process steps
         P = capacity, ton/day
         α = factor

The value of α for a well instrumented continuous operation is 10, for an operation with average labor requirement is 17, and for a batch operation with maximum labor is 23.

(v) Turnover ratio method

This method is suggested to estimate Plant cost. The method is expressed as (Humphreys, 1984):

$$TOR = \frac{GAS}{I} = \frac{P_u \times PR}{I}. \tag{3.10}$$

where   TOR = turnover ratio
         GAS = gross annual sales
         I = fixed capital investment
         P_u = unit price of sale
         PR = yearly production

The value of TOR can vary from 0.2 to 8, depending on the type of project/plant/industry. This method seems less accurate.

3.4.5. Detail Cost Estimation

Detail *or* final cost estimation should be performed based on detail design of the project (layout, drawing, item specification) and relevant associated factors.

3.4.5.1. Life Cycle Cost Elements
Life cycle costs of a building can include all costs of building ownership over its service life, including construction, maintenance and operation, recapitalization, and disposal.

Cost of an Equipment
Life cycle cost of an equipment may include the following (it is to be mentioned that a particular equipment may not need all the elements of cost):

- Purchase cost (coted rate plus tax, if applicable)
- Installation cost
- Training cost (training of staff to operate the equipment smoothly)
- Operating cost
    - Manpower cost (to operate the equipment)
    - Fuel/power cost
    - Special operating tool/item/lubricant cost (if any)
- Regular maintenance cost
- Spare parts cost (if needed)
- System upgrading cost (if applicable)
- Failure maintenance cost (if applicable)

Cost of Industrial or Large Project
For large commercial industry *or* project, the following costs may be involved in its life cycle:

- Infrastructural cost
    - Land acquisition cost
    - Survey, field engineering cost
    - Planning (including feasibility study), designing (architectural and structural) cost
    - Site preparation, demolition/replacement/alteration cost
    - Structural construction cost
    - Equipment cost
- Cost of associated system
    - License or permit fee (cost)
    - Relevant membership fee
    - Structural supervision cost
    - Inspection and testing, if applicable

- Operating cost
    - Land rent, if applicable
    - Land/infrastructure tax
    - Interest on capital invested, if applicable
    - Input item cost
    - Operating manpower/staff salary
    - System software cost
    - Technical data cost
    - Periodic renovation, if applicable
    - Owner's general office overhead cost
    - Staff's group insurance scheme cost
    - Support cost
    - Marketing/distribution cost
    - Logistic support cost (e.g. advertise in newspaper, radio, TV, seminar, workshop, campaign, donation, social work, etc.)
- Quality control cost
- Research and development cost
- Administrative cost
- Technical Consultant/Advisor fee
- Legal advisor fee
- Staff retirement-scheme cost
- Disposal/termination cost

It should remember that all of the above mentioned cost elements/items may not be applicable for all types of projects.

3.4.5.2. *Factors Affecting Life Cycle Cost*
For Machines or Equipments
Various factors may affect the total life-cycle cost of an equipment. These include:

- Purchase price
- Cost of installation
- Training cost of the staff
- Guarantee / warranty period
- Effective life
- Company's *or* supplier's servicing facility / availability of service center
- Price of spare parts
- Average failure rate, cost of failure (i.e. to remedy/rectify the failure)
- Required operator number, skill of the operator
- Safety measure requirement

For industrial project

- Equipment purchase cost
- Interest rate on the capital (if borrowed from Bank *or* other financial institute/organization)
- Effective life of the machine
- Service quality of the machine
- Number of the machine operator required
- Efficiency of the operators
- Price of the input, spare parts of the machine
- Output capacity and quality
- Price of the output, stability of the market price
- Competition with alternative products, etc.
- Indirect and miscellaneous cost
- Waste disposal/purification cost, if applicable
- Environmental pollution tax, if applicable

3.4.5.3. Estimation of Capital Cost

For a machine
For an industry
For a construction project

3.4.5.4. Estimation of Direct Cost

Elements of direct costs applicable to a proposed project (mentioned in earlier sections) should be calculated separately, and then should be aggregated. It should be calculated taking into account the cost elements, and using a suitable approach/method.

The general steps of estimating direct cost are described below:

(i) Determination of equipments, materials
(ii) Pricing the equipments, materials
(iii) Structural construction cost
(iv) Estimating labor hour requirement, labor number and costing
(v) Estimating requirement of management/supervising staff
(vi) Estimating salary of the staffs and other allowances
(vii) Input material cost for the factory
(viii) Materials testing and/or analysis cost
(ix) Waste disposal cost

Determination of equipments, materials and manpower/labor

Should be done based on the detail design and specification.

Pricing the equipments, materials

By direct cote, including the tax (if applicable).

Estimating labor hour requirement, labor number and costing
Estimating requirement of management/supervising staff

For different sections - such as administrative/supervisory, fiancé, marketing, research and development.

Estimating salary of the staffs and other allowances

Construction cost

Input material cost

To be determine according to detail operating schedule.

Materials testing and/or analysis cost

During production, testing and analysis of samples may be needed to ensure quality control.

Waste disposal cost

Waste disposal/treatment may be needed according to the State or Province environmental regulations/guidelines.

3.4.5.5. Estimation of Indirect Cost

As the indirect costs are not directly related to *or* linked to 'direct cost' (e.g. equipment cost, material cost, labor cost), its quantification and suggestion for generalized estimation method with accuracy is difficult. Indirect cost depends on:

- Type of the project
- Size of the project
- Project life span
- Surrounding environment (socio-economic, business, marketing competition, etc.)

For the construction firm *or* contractor, accurate estimation of indirect cost is essential to avid the chance of risk and to set value for competition to win the project bid (and also profit). In addition, accuracy in estimation will enhance the cost effectiveness in budget of projects nationally.

Several approaches have been suggested to estimate indirect cost of project. Some of them are listed below:

(a) Percentage of direct cost
(b) Calculation by components of indirect cost
(c) Using model

(a) 'Percentage of direct cost' method

In this approach, a certain percentage of direct cost of the project is considered as indirect cost. That is,

Indirect cost = P × Direct cost

where, P is the percentage (say, 10%, or 0.10).

Based on the idea of past project's indirect cost, the value of P can be taken. Mechanism of the indirect costing of large contractors involves their own standards which are set based on their past experiences and estimates.

For large projects (e.g. large industries, business companies), the percentage (P value) can be different for different sections of the project (e.g. production, general, administrative). In that case, total indirect cost will be the summation of indirect costs of different sections.

In labor intensive industries, some industry develop weighted labor rate, which combine monthly labor salary and monthly associated indirect costs.

For example, monthly labor salary of an industry is 1000 US$ and the overhead/indirect cost is 20%. Then the industry's monthly weighted labor salary is 1200 US$.

(b) Calculation by components of indirect cost

In this approach, indirect costs are calculated one by one component of indirect costs in accordance with project risk, project characteristics, and project value.

(c) Model for indirect cost

Regression model can be developed between indirect cost and pattern of the project – involving parameters of indirect cost. This model can then be used to estimate indirect cost of new project.

For different types of projects, different model should be developed. In addition, for small and large projects, the parameters and the associated coefficients may be different.

3.4.5.6. Miscellaneous/Contingency/Unforeseen Cost

The contingency amount may be included with each major cost items, or be included in a single category. The amount of contingency can be based on the past experience. However, for a new type of project, it can be based on the uncertainty of cost elements, variability of cost/price of the elements, and the difficulty of a particular project.

In general, for large project, 5 - 15 % of the project cost (other than the contingency – i.e. direct + indirect costs) is taken as contingency.

3.4.5.7. Some Other Relevant Points

In addition to the above mentioned cost elements, the following points should be taken into consideration with great care:

- − Assessment of social costs and benefits
- − Uncertainties in attribution of cost and benefit
- − Accurate estimation of financial costs, benefits
- − Financial viability and sustainability

Table 3.3. Detailed Budgetary Information of a research and development project (sample)

Summary of Budget (in TK): This is the outcome of what has been done in *A* to *G* below.

Line Item	Year-1	Year-2	Year-3	Sub-Total	% of grand total
A. Contractual Staff Salary	477000	477000	477000	1431000	14.9
B. Operating Expenses	300000	350000	315000	965000	10.0
C. Fuel, Oil and Maintenance	40000	170000	250000	460000	4.8
D. Field Research / Lab expenses and supplies	1250000	1420000	1170000	3840000	39.9
E. Publications and printing	30000	50000	200000	280000	2.9
F.Training/Workshop/Seminar etc.	30000	30000	330000	390000	4.0
G. Capital Expenses	960000	820000	0	1780000	18.5
H. Contingencies (5-10 %)	80000	80000	325000	485000	4.9
Grand Total	3167000	3397000	3067000	9631000	100

Summary of Budget (TK): 9631000/=

A. Contractual staff Salaries

Name, Designation and No.	Monthly Rate of Contractual Salary/Honoraria		
	Salary	Allowances	Total for one year
-Coordinator	-	-	
-Principal Investigator		20000	20000
Co-Principal Investigator		25000	25000
-Contractual Scientific Staff Including Research Students (Designation and No.) SSO (1) SO (1)	15000 10000	-	180000 120000
-Contractual Support Staff (Designation and No.) Scientific Assistant (1) Computer operator (1)	6000 5000	-	72000 60000
Total	36000	45000	**477000**

B. Operating Expenses

Line Item	Year-1	Year-2	Year-3	Total
Office Supplies/Services				
Stationary	40000	40000	50000	130000
Utilities	30000	30000	40000	100000
Computing	30000	50000	75000	155000
Traveling Allowances	200000	230000	150000	580000
Total	**300000**	**350000**	**315000**	**965000**

C. Fuel, Oil and Maintenance

Line Item	Year-1	Year-2	Year-3	Total
Fuel, Oil, Lubricants	20000	50000	50000	120000
Repair and Maintenance of Transport and Equipment	20000	120000	200000	340000
Total	**40000**	**170000**	**250000**	**460000**

D. Field Research/Lab Expenses and Supplies

Line Item	Year-1	Year-2	Year-3	Total
Seed, Fertilizer, Chemicals., etc	300000	400000	400000	1100000
Contract labor	200000	270000	270000	740000
Field Research expenses	300000	350000	200000	850000
Others: small reservoir/pond for rainwater harvesting, weather and storm data collection, vehicle hiring, etc.	450000	400000	300000	1150000
Total	**1250000**	**1420000**	**1170000**	**3840000**

E. Publications and Printing

Line Item	Year-1	Year-2	Year-3	Total
Publications	-	-	100000	100000
Printing	30000	50000	100000	180000
Total	**30000**	**50000**	**200000**	**280000**

F. Training/Workshops/Seminars etc.

Line Item	Year-1	Year-2	Year-3	Total
Training	30000	-	200000	230000
Workshops/Seminars etc.	-	30000	130000	160000
Total	**30000**	**30000**	**330000**	**390000**

G. Capital Expenses

Line Item	Year-1	Year-2	Year-3	Total
Furniture and Supplies (Cup bord-2, Computer table-3, Computer chair-3, File cabinet-2, Chair-3, Guest chair-6, Side table -3, lab tool -10, Still almira-2)	150000	101000	-	251000
Small Equipment, Tools, etc. (Electrical oven-1, Electrical strear-1, core sampler-1set, Ice box-2, Soil auger-2, Sprayer machine-2, Electrical balance-2, Top loading balance-2, Portable EC meter-2, Pump and electrical motor, Laptop-2 computer-3, printer-2, spirel binder -1, scaner-2, laminating machine-1, curter machine-1,digital camera-2, Mobile set for weather station-2, Telephone set-2, fax machine and some glass wares)	600000	519000	-	1119000
Small Transport (Two-wheeler: Motor cycle-2, Bicycle-2)	210000	200000	-	410000
Total	**960000**	**820000**	**-**	**1780000**

H. Contingencies (Only those items which are not covered by earlier heads)

Line Item	Year-1	Year-2	Year-3	Total
Internet	40000	40000	40000	120000
Photocopy	40000	40000	35000	115000
Supporting staff honoraria	-	-	250000	250000
Total	**80000**	**80000**	**325000**	**485000**

3.4.6. Cost Elements of Different Engineering Structures

For general idea and conception, the major cost elements of different engineering structures are mentioned below. For a particular situation, it may vary.

Bridge
- Design fee
- Consultation fee (including supervision)
- Temporary facility development (structural, water, electricity)
- Earthwork
- De-watering (if needed)
- Pilling
- Normal structural cost (materials + staff salary)
- Material removal cost (if any)
- Contingency

Building
- Design fee (architectural and structural)
- Permit fee
- Supervision fee
- Temporary facility development (structural, water, electricity) cost (for the construction staffs/labors)
- Earthwork
- Construction material cost (including transportation cost)
- Essential (e.g. water, electricity, gas, sanitation, drainage) facility development cost
- Labor cost (or construction cost, as a whole)
- Painting cost (if desired)
- Contingency

3.4.7. Examples on Cost Estimation

Example 3.6.

A 500 MW nuclear power generation station has been built in an area spending US$ 200 million. To meet the local demand, additional 300 MW power is necessary. Estimate the cost of the new plant (300 MW). Assume Cost-Capacity factor of 0.8.

Soln

We know, the Cost-capacity relation, $C_n = C_0 \left[\frac{K_n}{K_0}\right]^{\alpha}$

Given:

Capacity of old (but recent) power station, $K_0 = 500$ MW

Capacity of New power station, $K_n = 300$,,

Cost of old power station, $C_0 = 200$ million US$

Cost-Capacity factor, $\alpha = 0.8$
Cost for new capacity, $C_n = ?$

Putting the values in above equation, we obtain, $C_n = 200 \times \left[\frac{300}{500}\right]^{0.8}$
= 132.9079612   US$ (**Ans.**)

Example 3.7.

A solid-fluid processing plant's delivered equipment cost is US$ 2.3 million. Estimate the total cost of the plant installation.

Soln
We know, total plant cost according to 'Lang factor method',
TPC = n × DEC

Given:
Delivered equipment cost, DEC = 2.3 million US$
For solid-fluid processing plant, n = 3.6 (as suggested by Lang)
      Thus,   TPC   =3.6 × 2.3
                      = 8.28 million US$ (**Ans.**)

Example 3.8.

An industry is producing 80,000 items per year. The selling price of each item is $50. Assuming a turnover ratio of 3, calculate the capital investment for the industry.

Soln
We get, turn-over ratio,

$$TOR = \frac{GAS}{I} = \frac{P_u \times PR}{I}$$

Given:
Yearly production, PR = 80,000 items
Unit price of each item, P_u = $ 50
Turnover ratio, TOR = 3
Fixed capital investment, I = ?

Putting the values in above equation,

$$3 = \frac{50 \times 80,000}{I}$$

Or, I = 1333333 $ (**Ans.**)

Example 3.9.

The trend equation of cost to set up a chemical industry is expressed as:

C = 12000 + 1.2 Y

where, Y is the year of accomplishment; and C is in US$. Estimate the cost of set up of a similar industry in 2015.

Soln

Given:

Trend eqn., C = 12000 + 1.2 Y

Year of accomplishment, Y = 2015

Thus, C = 12000 + 1.2 × 2015

= 14418 US$ **(Ans.)**

Example 3.10.

A power generation company has built 75 MW solar electricity generation plant with US$ 1.4 million in a remote area. To meet the local demand, additional 100 MW power is necessary. Estimate the cost of the new plant to meet the local demand (100 MW). Assume standard Cost-Capacity factor.

Soln

We know, the Cost-capacity relation, $C_n = C_0 \left[\frac{K_n}{K_0}\right]^\alpha$

Given:

Capacity of old power station, K_0 = 75 MW

Capacity of New power station, K_n =100 MW

Cost of old power station, C_0 = 1.4 million US$

Cost for new capacity, C_n = ?

Assuming Cost-Capacity factor, α = 0.8

Putting the values in above equation, we obtain, $C_n = 1.4 \times \left[\frac{100}{75}\right]^{0.8}$

= 1. 76 million US$ **(Ans.)**

Example 3.11.

The historical cost data relevant to a proposed project are given below. Derive the *cost equation*, and estimate the cost of similar project (similar type and of similar size) to be implemented in year 2015.

Year	Cost (US$)
1990	80,000
2000	95,000
2006	100,000
2010	105,000

Soln

Plotting the data points with *Year* in X-axis and *Cost* in Y-axis (in Microsoft Excel), we obtain linear trend line as follows:

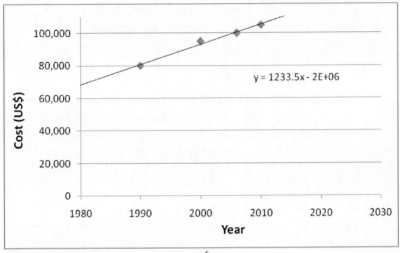

The trend equation is: $Y = 1233.5X - 2 \times 10^6$

For the year 2015, the cost = $(1233.5 \times 2015) - (2 \times 10^6)$
$$= 485502.5 \text{ US\$ } \textbf{(Ans.)}$$

Example 3.12.

For a proposed industrial project, the price and number of different items under different sub-sections are given below. Estimate the total cost of the project.

Sub-section	Number of items	Unit price/cost (US$)
Machine	1000	750
Space for each machine, 12 ft^2	1000	800
Office space for management staffs, 400 ft^2	01	30,000

Assume '*Contingency cost*' as 10% of the above costs.

Soln

Sub-section	Number of items	Unit price/cost (US$)	Sub-section cost (item number × unit price), US$
Machine	1000	750	750000
Space for each machine, 12 ft^2	1000	800	800000
Office space for management staffs, 400 ft^2	01	30,000	30000
Total direct cost, US$			1580000
Contingency cost', @ 10% of direct cost =			158000
Grand total cost = total direct cost + contingency cost =			**1738000**

Thus, total cost of the project = US$ 1738000 **(Ans.)**

Example 3.13.

The total construction cost of a 'Palm Oil Refinery' having output capacity of 10,000 litre/day at Kuantan, Malaysia, completed in 2011 was US$ 10 million. It is proposed to build a similar refinery (same capacity) at Kuala Lumpur, to be completed in 2015. Estimate the cost of the proposed plant.

Soln

Here, the capacity is similar, only the time difference for installation is the factor for variation of cost. Neglecting the locational effect of cost variation, the escalation of price over the time and/or inflation rate (or vice versa) is the factor for increase (or decrease) in price.

Assuming a combined increasing rate for both general escalation of price and inflation, 3% per annum, the cost in 2015 can be calculated as:

$F = P(1+r)^N$
Given:
P = 10 million US$
r = 3% = 0.03
N = 2015 – 2011 = 4 yrs
Putting the values, F = 11. 69 million US$ **(Ans.)**

Example 3.14.

The total construction cost of a previously (in 2010) constructed building is expressed as follows:

$C = 2260 + 250 \times P$
where
C = total construction cost, US$
P = area of the building, ft^2
For the additional information given below, estimate the cost of a similar building in a new area having floor area of 2000 ft^2.
Additional information:
Construction year: 2013
Inflation rate: 1.5 % per year
Local index of construction cost: 1.05

Soln
The cost function is:
$C = 2260 + 250 \times P$

For the New one, P =2000 ft^2
Thus, Cost as per cost function, $C_f = 2260 + 250 \times 2000 = 502260$ US$
Given, local cost index =1.05
Adjusting the cost for the local index, $C_l = 502260 \times 1.05 = 527373$ US$
Time difference, N = 2013 -2010 = 3 yrs

Inflation rate = 1.05 %

Adjusted cost for the inflation, $C_i = C_l (1+r)^N = 527373 \times (1+1.05/100)^3$

= 551462.5 US$ **(Ans.)**

Exercise

Section – Data source and design capacity estimation

1. Discuss the importance of accurate data collection for economic analysis.
2. Identify and discuss the types of data required for economic analysis.
3. Explain, how you will forecast supply of natural resources for design purpose.
4. Identify and discuss different sources of published data (at least 05 nos)
5. Discuss the potentials (or advantages) and limitations (or disadvantages) of different types of data. Mention the data checking procedure.
6. Discuss the factors to be considered in predicting the demand.
7. Discuss the considerations / 'actions to be taken' in case of: (a) no data available, (b) analysis at global level.
8. Identify different source-department for data of different types of work.
9. In an area, total population in 2011 is 2.0 million. If the average population growth rate in the area during this period is 2.1%, what would be the population in that area in 2050,?
10. Total population in an area in 2008 was 8.0 million. What would be the population in that area in 2025, if the average population growth rate in the area during this period is 1.6 %?
11. A 'Food and Beverage' Company at Alaska City is planning to set up its production capacity based on local demand. After a survey of market demand, it is found that the present (year 2013) demand per day is 300 items. The company is targeting its capacity 10 years ahead, that is to capable of satisfying the demand in year 2025. It is expected that due to increase in population, the demand will increase by 20% of the present in year 2025. What should be the design production capacity of the industry?
12. In a new proposed town at Gambang, Malaysia, the present design population is 1200 and daily per capita water demand is projected to 140 litre. As an Executive Engineer of that locality, you are going to design water-supply project. You are planning the water supply capacity for 30 years projection. Expected average population increase during this period is 2% per annum, and the increase in per capita water-demand due to change in income during the projected period is expected to10%. Determine the design capacity of the water-supply project.
13. In a new resort city at Victoria, Australia, the present population is 2000 and daily per capita water demand (normal demand) is 160 litre (including household, gardening, car washing, etc.). But there is a deficit of water by 5% of the demand. As an Executive Engineer of the City Corporation, you are going to submit a water-supply project to the higher authority. For that purpose, you will perform economic analysis of different supply options for the projected demand. You are planning the project for 25 yrs projection. Expected average population increase (growth rate) during this period is 2.5% per annum, and the increase in per capita water-demand

due to change in income is expected to 9%. Determine the design capacity of the water-supply project.

Hints: Design capacity = present deficit + normal demand for the increased (new) people + extra demand due to change in income for the total people.

14. The 'Jamuna Group of Industries' is planning to set up an industry at Alberta City to produce 'Cosmetic items'. The company is planning to fix its production capacity based on local demand. After a survey of market demand, it is found that the present (year 2013) demand per day is 1000 items. The company is targeting its capacity 10 years ahead. It is expected that due to increase in population, the demand will increase by 8% of the present; and also due to change in habit as a result of increase in per capita income, demand will increase by 5%. What should be the design 'production capacity' of the industry?

Section – Cost estimation

1. Why correct estimation of project cost is important?
2. Define the following: Recurring cost, contingency, annuity, project
3. Briefly discuss the stages of cost estimation with procedures.
4. What are the approaches of cost estimation? Briefly discuss.
5. Describe various preliminary cost estimation methods along with the formula.
6. What are the life cycle cost elements of: (a) An equipment, (b) Industrial project
7. Discuss the factors affecting life cycle cost of: (a) An equipment, (b) Industrial project
8. Mention the general steps of estimating direct cost.
9. Briefly describe the issues/importance and approaches of indirect cost estimation.
10. What are the general procedures of estimating contingency cost?
11. Mention the cost elements of the following structures/plants: Bridge, building, hydroelectric power plant, sluice gate, waste water treatment plant
12. A 250 MW hydropower generation plant has been built with US$ 2.5 million. There is enough hydro-source to build another 500 MW generation plant. Calculate the cost of the 500 MW plant, if the Cost-Capacity factor is 0.75.
13. A power generation company has built 50 MW solar electricity generation plant with US$ 1.0 million in a remote area. To meet the local demand, additional 100 MW power is necessary. Estimate the cost of the new plant to meet the local demand (100 MW). Assume standard Cost-Capacity factor.
14. The total construction cost of a chemical industry having output capacity of ethanol of 10,000 litre/day, completed in 2012 was US$ 12 million. It is proposed to build a similar industry, to be completed in 2015. Estimate the cost of the proposed industry. Assume standard value of relevant missing data.
15. The total construction cost of a previously (in 2011) constructed building is expressed as follows:

$$C = 2200 + 200 \times P$$

where C = total construction cost, US$
        P = area of the building, ft^2

For the additional information given below, estimate the cost of a similar building in a new area having floor area of 2000 ft^2.

Additional information:
Construction year: 2014
Inflation rate: 1.1 % per year
Local index of construction cost: 1.02

16. A heat exchanger's delivered equipment cost is US$ 500. Estimate the total cost of its installation.
17. An industry is producing 75,000 items per year. The selling price of each item is $30. Assuming a turnover ratio of 2, calculate the capital investment for the industry.
18. A 50 MW Coal power generation plant has been built in an area spending US$ 100 million. To meet the local demand, additional 30 MW power is necessary. Estimate the cost of the new plant. Assume standard Cost-Capacity factor.
19. The historical cost data relevant to a proposed project are given below. Derive the *cost equation*, and estimate the cost of similar project (similar type and of similar size) to be implemented in year 2020.

Year	Cost (US$)
1990	60,000
1995	75,000
2000	90,000
2010	100,000

20. The total construction cost of a Petrol Refinery having output capacity of 5,000 litre/day at Pahang, Malaysia, completed in 2010 was US$ 8 million. It is proposed to build a similar refinery at Kuala Lumpur, to be completed in 2015. Estimate the cost of the proposed plant

REFERENCES

Hand, W.E. (1958). From flow sheet to cost estimate. *Petroleum Refiner*, 37: 331-334.

Humphreys, K.K. (edit.) (1984). *Project and cost engineering handbook*, Marcel Dekker, Inc., New York, p.51-57.

Lang, H.J. (1947). Simplified approach to preliminary cost estimates. *Chemical Engineering*, 54: 130-133.

Chapter 4

FUNDAMENTALS AND THEORIES OF FINANCIAL ANALYSIS FOR PROJECT EVALUATION

4.1. BACKGROUND

The purpose of economic analysis of engineering (and also for other) projects is to increase the net output measured at economic prices in the national economy. An investment or intervention is said to be economically efficient when it maximizes the value of output from the resources available. In economic and financial decision making, we need the following types of evaluation:

-   testing the economic viability of a project
-   choice of the best one among project alternatives, and
-   choice of the least-cost option for achieving the same benefits

4.2. FINANCIAL ANALYSIS

Financial analysis is an important part of the process of developing a business plan/industry/development project and then for monitoring the success of that plan. Full financial analysis in the form typically adapted by industrial accounting today is for decision making and the development of strategic plans.

Typical elements of financial analysis include:

(1) *Budgeting* - Creating a budget setting out planned cash flows in and out of the business. By monitoring a cash flow budget, it is possible to identify any potential crisis points where liquidity will be poor. Budgets can also be set out for income and expenditure by the business, as well as a capital budget showing major capital spending e.g. on premises, equipment etc.

(2) *Profit and loss analysis* - This involves the creation of a profit and loss budget setting out expected future profits/losses for the business. This is important in assessing the return on the business.

(3) *Balance sheet* – Developing a balance sheet is a financial "snapshot" of your business at a given date in time. It includes your assets and liabilities and your business' net worth over the forecast horizon.

(4) *Cash flow statement* – Summarizes the company's cash receipts and cash disbursements over a period of time; lists cash to and cash from operating, investing, and financing activities, along with the net increase or decrease in cash for the period.

(5) *Solvency analysis* - Involves calculating the net current assets of a business as shown in the balance sheet (i.e. current assets - current liabilities).

(6) *Return on capital employed* - This is a measure of the return made on all of the capital employed in the business in a given period of time.

4.3. DIFFERENT FINANCIAL INDICES AND RELATED TERMINOLOGIES

Present and Future Value

Present value tells the current worth of a future sum of money. Future value gives one the future value (at a future date) of cash that one have now. Both of this has practical implication. For example, you have $2000 saving and will start to save $500 per month in an account that yields 6% per year. You will make your deposit at the end of each month.

You want to know the value of your investment in 5 years, or the future value of your savings account. For a multi-year project, future values of the present values (and near future cash flows, if any) are calculated at the end of the project life.

Least Cost Analysis

Least-cost analysis aims at identifying the least-cost project option for supplying output to meet forecasted demand. This method applies to projects where the benefits can be valued, or to projects where the benefits take the form of a single commodity. Least-cost analysis involves comparing the costs of the various mutually exclusive, technically feasible project options and selecting the one with the lowest cost. For multi-year project, the alternative with the lowest present value of costs (for desired output) is the least-cost alternative. For example, it may be that the cheapest way of increasing water supply is through more efficient management of the existing supply rather than through augmenting capacity.

Cost Effectiveness

In some cases, the benefits or outcomes of a project cannot be valued (or not directly measurable), but can be quantified or have a specific outcome. For example, in a pollution control project, the outcome is pollution control (having specific quality or grade), with a specific cost. To attain a specific grade of pollution control, different methods or techniques can be employed and their cost may be different. Cost-effectiveness analysis is an analysis that seeks to find the best alternative activity, process, or intervention that minimizes cost.

A measure of the cost effectiveness is obtained by measuring costs against outcome (average incremental economic cost). The cost effectiveness ratio – the cost per unit change in quality (improving certain quality, lessening hazardous effect, etc.) for each of the alternative methods are compared. The technique or method that needs minimum cost to attain targeted outcome is most cost effective. Analysis of cost effectiveness allows choosing the least-cost project evaluating various options.

There may be circumstances where the project alternatives have more than one outcome. In order to assess the cost effectiveness in such a case, it is necessary to devise a testing system where the outcomes of different dimensions can be added together.

It is also necessary to select some weights for adding the different dimensions reflecting their relative importance in relation to the objectives of the project. Such a use of cost-effectiveness analysis is called *weighted cost-effectiveness analysis*.

Initial Investment

It is the investment made at the beginning of a project. The initial investment may include hardware (cost of buying and installing the machine, structural setup), software, startup costs, licensing fees, etc. Since most of the projects involve initial cash outflow, its value is usually negative.

Salvage Value

It is the money that can be gained by selling the hardware or instruments at the end of the project. If there is, the amount would be added to the income amount, normally at the last year of the project.

Nominal and real value (cost, benefit, interest rate)

The real value is one where the effects of inflation have been factored, whereas, a nominal value is one where the effects of inflation have not been accounted for. To account for inflation, either real or nominal values may be used, but with consistently. That is, nominal costs and benefits require nominal discount rates, and real costs and benefits require real discount rates.

The real interest is one where the effects of inflation have been factored in. A nominal interest is one where the effects of inflation have not been accounted for. That is,

Real interest rate = Nominal interest rate - Inflation

Inflation is positive. So, the real interest rate is lower than the nominal interest rate. If the inflation rate is negative (i.e. deflation), then the real interest rate will be larger than the nominal interest rate.

Income Stream or Cash Flow

An income stream is a series of amounts of money. Each amount of money comes in or goes out at some specific time, either now or in the future. Sample example of an income stream is given below:

Year	0	1	2	3	4	5
Income amounts	-$2000	$500	$600	$700	$600	$600

The net cash flow for each year of the project is the difference between revenue (or benefit) and cost. All the amounts in the income stream are net income, meaning that each is revenue minus cost, or income minus outgo. In the year 0, the cost exceeds the revenue by $2000. Negative income is cost, or outgo, which represent the cost of buying and installing the machine. In the year 1 to 5, the revenue exceeded the cost. The investment evidently has no salvage value. If there were, the amount that could be realized from the sale would be added to the income amount for the year 5. For simplicity, the cash flow in the above example has at one-year intervals, but real time investments can have cash flow at irregular times. But the principles of evaluation are the same for all cases.

Cash Flow Diagrams

A cash flow diagram is a picture of a financial problem that shows all cash inflows and outflows plotted along a horizontal time line. It can help you to visualize a financial problem.

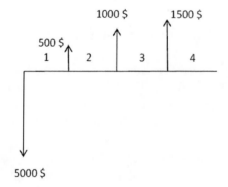

Figure 4.1. Schematic of cash-flow diagram.

Constructing a Cash-Flow Diagram

The time line is a horizontal line divided into equal periods such as days, months, or years. Each cash-flow, such as an investment (or cost) or receipt (revenue), is plotted along this line at the beginning or end of the period in which it occurs.

The outcomes *or* revenues (*or* the series of deposits in case of Bank scheme) are positive cash inflows (that are represented by arrows extending upward from the line, with their bases at the appropriate positions along the line), and the costs (*or* withdrawal in case of Bank scheme) are negative outflow (that are represented by arrows which extend downward from the time line).

Internal rate of return is traditionally defined as the discount rate at which NPV is equal to zero. It is the projected discount rate that makes the NPV of a project equal to zero. It is one of the capital budgeting methods used by firms to decide whether they should make long-term investments. It helps making decision about which project is most economical for a particular situation.

Discounting

Discounting is a procedure developed by economists to evaluate investments that produce future income. It is the process by which the values of future effects are adjusted to render them comparable to the values placed on current costs and benefits. It is accomplished by multiplying the future value(s) by 'discount factor' / 'discount rate'.

Discount Rate

A percentage rate representing the rate at which the value of equivalent benefits and costs decrease in the future compared to the present. The discount rate is used to determine the present value of the future benefit and cost streams.

The rate can be based on the alternative economic return in other uses given up by committing resources to a particular project, or on the preference for consumption benefit today rather than later. The economic net present value is generally calculated for each project alternative using the Bank interest rate.

Compounding

It is the process whereby the values of present effects are adjusted to render them comparable to the values placed on future consumption, costs, and benefits.

Discounted Cash Flow

The discounted cash flow approach describes a method to value a project or an entire company using the concepts of the time value of money. It is widely used in investment finance, real estate development, corporate financial management and other development projects. All future cash flows are estimated and discounted to give them a present value. Discounted cash flow (DCF) includes the present value (PV) and the internal rate of return (IRR) methods of analyzing cash flows. The DCF provides insight into financial management.

The discounted cash flow formula is derived from the future value formula for calculating the time value of money and compounding returns.

$$FV = PV \times (1+i)^n \qquad\qquad (4.1)$$

where
    FV = future value
    PV = present value
    i = interest rate (or time value of money)
    n = number of year

For single cash flow in one future period, discounted cash flow equation can be expressed as:

$$DPV = \frac{FV}{(1+r)^n}$$

where
    DPV = discounted present value of the future cash flow (FV)
    r = discount rate

In case of cash flows in multiple time periods, discounted present value is the sum of the individual present values, expressed as:

$$DPV = \sum_{t=0}^{N} \frac{FV_t}{(1+r)^t} \qquad\qquad (4.2)$$

where t = time period (year number from the present year).

Payback Period (P_p)
"Payback Period" is the time required to recover the initial cost of an investment/project.

Calculation of Payback Period
In some text Book, P_p for even cash-flow is *wrongly defined* as:
P_p = (Investment required)/(Net annual cash-flow),
    Which requires regular and uniform annual cash-flow, and that it does not account for the 'time value of money'.
Ideally, "Payback Period" is the year at which the 'Cumulative discounted net cash-flow' is zero. If the condition does not exist, it should be computed as follows:

(a) If the cash-flow occurs regularly over periods, the 'Payback Period' can be computed as:

    P_p = (Last year with a negative 'Cumulative discounted net cash-flow') + (Absolute value of net cash-flow in that year)/(Net cash-flow in the preceding year)

(b) For irregular cash-flow, the 'Payback Period' can be taken as the "First year with a positive *Cumulative discounted net cash-flow*".

4.4. EXPRESSION OF COST AND BENEFIT

In different projects, investment (or input requirement) and the return (or outcome) do not follow same time. Thus, they are not directly measurable. To overcome this problem, the inputs and outputs are converted to an equivalent amount. There are different ways to express and compare costs and benefits that occur in multiple time periods on a consistent basis. Procedures for calculating cost and benefit that occur in more than one time period are:

a) Net present value (NPV)
b) Net future value (NFV)
c) Annualized value

In NPV, discounting places all costs and benefits at the present time period; in NFV, accumulation places them at a future time; and annualization spreads them smoothly over time. Among the three procedures, net present value method is widely used.

4.4.1. Net Future Value

Net future value (NFV) is a way of rendering cost and benefit that occur in more than one time period. Net future value is the total future value of all cash flows. It is an estimate of what the principal will become over time. For example, assuming a compound rate of 8 %, present value of $5000 ten year from now would be $ 10794.62.

The NFV value of a projected stream of current and future costs and benefits is obtained by multiplying the benefits and costs in each year by a time dependent weight, d_t, and adding all of the weighted as follows:

$$NFV = d_0NB_0 + d_1NB_1 + d_2NB_2 + ...+ d_{n-1}NB_{n-1} + d_nNB_n. \qquad (4.3)$$

where, NB_t is the difference between benefits and costs that accrue in year t, and the accumulation weights (also termed as compound factor), d_t, is given by:

$$d_t = (1+r)^{(n-t)}$$

where, r is the discount rate. Thus, the equn. (4.3) can be written as:

$$NFV = \sum_{t=0}^{n} NB_t (1+r)^{(n-t)} \qquad (4.4)$$

4.4.2. Annualized Values

Annualized value, AV (*or* Annual equivalent value) is the value of an *equivalent uniform annual series* of cash flow. That is, in annualized approach, the total value is spread up throughout its effective life uniformly. In the literature, it is also titled as Annual Worth

(AW), Equivalent Annual Worth (EAW), Annual Equivalent (AE), etc. For cost series, it is termed as Equivalent Annual Cost, Equivalent Uniform Annual Cost, etc.

In calculating AV, the irregular cash flow of the entire effective service life is transformed into an annuity (a constant annual value paid every year) for the same service life. It can be calculated from Present Value (PV) *or* Future Value (FV).

The annualized value is calculated from the present value (PV) by using the following formula:

$$AV = PV \frac{i(1+i)^n}{(1+i)^n - 1} \tag{4.5}$$

where, i is the interest rate, n is the effective life/service life of the project.

For example, in the absence of discount rate, a cost of US$ 1,000 becomes US$ 2,000 at the end of first year, US$ 3,000 at the end of second year, US$ 4,000 at the end of third year. From that, it can be said that, cost US$1,000 per year is annualized costs over the three years period. Costs and benefits may be annualized separately by using a two-step process.

Comparing annualized costs to annualized benefits is equivalent to comparing the present values of costs and benefits. To compare average cost effectiveness among alternative policy options, divide the annualized cost by annualized benefit (such as cost per 100 m^3 water loss avoided, cost per meter groundwater depletion avoided).

4.4.3. Net Present Value

4.4.3.1. Concept and Definition

Net present value is the difference between the present value of the benefit stream and the present value of the cost stream for a project. The word '*net*' in '*net present value*' indicates that the calculation includes the initial costs as well as the subsequent cost and benefit. Costs and benefits of a development project or a technology frequently occur at different times.

The NPV of the time-phased costs over the economic life of an investment project is the best single-number measure of its life-cycle cost.

4.4.3.2. Derivation of NPV

If we assume that income comes (benefit) or goes (cost) in annual bursts, the net present value (NPV) value of a projected stream of current and future costs and benefits is obtained by multiplying the benefits and costs in each year by a time dependent weight, d_t, and adding all of the weighted as follows:

$$NPV = NB_0 + d_1 NB_1 + d_2 NB_2 + \ldots + d_{n-1} NB_{n-1} + d_n NB_n \tag{4.6}$$

$$= NB_0 + \sum_{t=1}^{n} d_t NB_t$$

where, NB_t is the difference between benefits and costs that accrue in year t, n is the final period in the future (n= t), and the discounting weight, (also termed as discount factor), d_t, is given by:

$$d_t = 1/(1+r)^t$$

where, r is the discount rate. Thus, the equation can be written as:

$$NPV = NB_0 + \sum_{t=1}^{n} \frac{NB_t}{(1+r)^t} \qquad (4.7)$$

As the initial investment is a cost, it is treated as negative benefit.

That is, NPV = (- Initial investment) + $\sum$ (Net cash flows at year t)/ $(1+r)^t$

4.5. ANALYSIS OF NET PRESENT VALUE (NPV)

Analysis of net present value requires four basic steps:

- Forecast the benefits and costs in each year.
- Determine a discount rate.
- Use a formula to calculate the NPV
- Compare the NPVs of the alternatives.

Step 1: Forecasting the Benefits and Costs

Accurate forecasting of future costs and benefits can be the most difficult and critical step in NPV and as a whole in project financial analysis. All possible costs and benefits of the proposed project should be taken into account, including non-monetary costs and benefits. A 'sunk cost' should be ignored in the analysis for multiple options. It is the cost that will be same regardless of the alternate options. For example, cost for survey of the project area.

Cost Forecasting

The costs should include:

- Input cost
- Operational cost
- Maintenance cost
- Opportunity cost of the inputs/resources
- Uncertain cost

Input Cost

All sorts of input costs (both fixed and variable) should be considered in analysis. Salaries of the project manager and other staffs, fee of the consultant, etc. fall under this category.

Opportunity Cost

The opportunity cost of a project is the potential benefits that are lost by selecting the project. More specifically, it is equal to the net benefit that is to be achieved from alternate use of the resources (capital, human resources, or other major inputs).

For example, a project has been proposed to develop an agricultural farm for crop production over a land of 100 hectares. If the farm is not developed, the farmer will get 5000 US$ per annum as hire for cattle grazing without any investment. Now, $5000 is to be added to the total cost as opportunity cost. If this opportunity cost is not included as cost in project analysis, then some proposals may appear to be better because they are using existing resources free.

Operational Cost

This includes salary of the laborers, fuel cost for the machines (for agricultural project fuel cost, tractors fertilizers, insecticides), etc.

Maintenance cost

This category includes repair cost of the instruments, computers, cars, etc.

Uncertain Cost

Sometimes it is difficult to estimate the cost because they are dependent on an unpredictable environment. In such uncertain case, still it is possible to make an estimate (expected value).

Step 2: Determination of Discount Rate

The discount rate converts the stream of future costs and benefits into their value today. The process of discounting is needed due to the time value of money and inflation, and therefore discount rate should be determined based on the aforementioned two factors. For convenience, sometimes it is taken equal to the bank interest rate.

Consistent decision making requires that the same discount rate be used for both benefit and cost, if net benefit is not used. Moreover, the same discount rate must be used for different alternative options.

Impact of Discount Rate on NPV Estimates

In general, the NPV estimate varies with the discount rate. But under some circumstances, the NPV may be very sensitive to discount rate. When costs and benefits of a project are largely constant over the time period, discounted costs and benefits will produce almost same conclusion regarding the project acceptance or rejection. Only, the higher discount rate will reduce the NPV. Discount rate may significantly affect the NPV estimates when there is a substantial difference in the timing and amount of costs and benefits. We may consider a project where all the costs are incurred at the starting (or first year) of the project, but the benefits will occur over 50 years period. In such case, the costs are not discounted but the benefit will do. Hence, the NPV here will depend critically on the discount rate used.

Step 3: Calculation of Net Present Value

At first, calculate the net benefit for each year by subtracting the cost from the benefit. Then, calculate the net present value for the net benefit of each year using the formula given below:

$$NPV_n = \frac{NB_n}{(1+r)^n} \qquad (4.8)$$

where

NPV_n = net present value for the year n

NB_n = net benefit for the year n

n = chronological serial number of the year in the cash flow series for which the NPV is calculating

In the above equation, the time dependent weighting factor, is termed as discounting factor. In NPV calculation, for simplicity, it is assumed that the discount rate will not change over the life of the project.

Sum up the NPVs to get total NPV. Similarly, calculate NPVs for the alternatives. The procedure has been explained below with sample examples.

The main limitation of NPV analysis is the difficulty of accurately forecasting future costs and benefits.

Step 4: Compare the NPVs of the Alternatives

The NPVs of the alternatives are compared and a decision is taken. The net present value calculated at the Banks discount rate should be greater than zero for a project to be acceptable. A positive net present value means the investment is better. A negative net present value means the alternative investment, or not borrowing, is better.

4.6. THE NPV CURVE

The NPV curve shows the relationship between the discount rate and the net present value for a range of discount rates (Figure 4.1).

With net-positive cash flows, NPV decreases from maximum at a zero percent discount rate and converges on zero as it increases.

Once past zero NPV, where IRR is determined, NPV is negative at all discount rate. The curve shows the net present value for a discount rate of 0 to 12. The curve crosses the horizontal line (indicating NPV = 0) between 0.04 and 0.06.

So the internal rate of return is between 0.04 and 0.06 (nearly at 0.05). Thus the internal rate of return is 0.05.

The NPV curve can be represented by the formula:

$$NPV = I_0 + \frac{I_1}{1+r} + \frac{I_2}{(1+r)^2} + \cdots\cdots + \frac{I_n}{(1+r)^n} \qquad (4.9)$$

where I_0 is the initial investment, I_i is the income amount for the specific year i ($i = 0$ to n), and r is the discount rate. This is similar for the net present value for annualized costs and revenues with a constant discount rate.

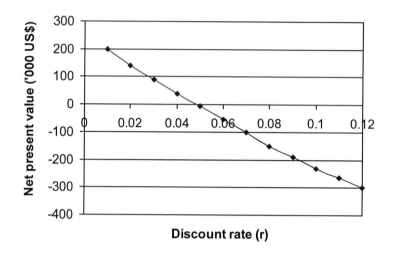

Figure 4.2. The NPV curve.

4.7. DISCOUNTING / COMPOUNDING FORMULA UNDER DIFFERENT PERSPECTIVES

The following situations of cash-flow are considered here for mathematical derivation:

a) Single installment /cash-flow of money
b) Uniform annual cash-flow
c) Discrete non-uniform annual cash-flow

4.7.1. Single Installment/Cash-Flow of Money

In this case, the aim is to convert the amount at one date to an equivalent value at another date. More specifically, the present value is converted to a future value (compounding), or the future value is converted to an equivalent present value (discounting).

4.7.1.1. Single Installment Compounding

Let us assume that P is the present income (or cost *or* investment) amount and we want to know its future value after n years (that is, what amount it will be). To do this, we have to know the rate of return per year of the investment. Let r is the rate of return (in percent) per year of the investment for the prevailing condition. After 1(one) year, the amount will be:

P + P × r = P(1+r) [Here, Pr is the earnest money from the capital P]

This amount, P(1+r), is the capital for the second year. After second year, the amount will be compounded to:

$$P(1+r) + [P(1+r) \times r] = P(1+r) [1+r] = P(1+r)^2$$

Similarly, after 3 (three) years, the amount will be compounded to $P(1+r)^3$
Therefore, after N years, the amount will be: $P(1+r)^N$
Let we express the compounded amount after N years (future value) by the symbol F. Thus,

$$F = P(1+r)^N \qquad (4.10)$$

That is, we can say,
Future value of any present amount = (Present amount) $\times (1 + \text{rate of return})^N$
where, N is the number of years into the future that the income amount will be received.
Here, the factor (1+r) is termed as accumulation weight *or* compound factor.

4.7.1.2. Single Installment Discounting

From equation. (4.10), we can write:

$$P = \frac{F}{(1+r)^N} \qquad .(4.11)$$

Here, the factor $\dfrac{1}{1+r}$ is termed as discounting weight *or* discount factor, and P is the present value to a future value, F.

4.7.1.3 Annual compounding for multiple payments

Assume an income stream where *m* is the number of payment per year. In this case, annual rate of return (r) can be split as *r/m*, and the future accumulation can be computed as:

$$F = P(1+r/m)^{Nm} \qquad (4.12)$$

4.7.2. Uniform Annual Cash-Flow

4.7.2.1. Compounding for Uniform Yearly Installment

Assume a project having period of N years where benefit (income) comes (or cost goes) in annual basis, and the yearly amount is uniform throughout the project period, and it is denoted by A_y. We want to know the accumulated amount of benefit at the end of N years.

Here, the income from the project for the year N (last income) will not subject to compound because it will come at the end of Nth year. Thus, the actual time period for compounding is (N-1) year. The income of year 1, 2, 3, ...(N-1) will be compounded for year (N-1), (N-2), (N-3), ...1 year, respectively.

We know, compounded amount from single income at the end of N year = $P(1+r)^N$, where N is the number of years for which it is compounded.

In our present case, the income will be available at the end of each year. Thus, if we apply compound formula (from starting to ending of period) and add them to obtain the total future value, F, then:

$$F = A_y [(1+r)^{N-1} + (1+r)^{N-2} + \ldots\ldots\ldots\ldots + (1+r)^2 + (1+r) + 1 + 0]$$

Rearranging,

$$F = A_y [1 + (1+r) + (1+r)^2 + \ldots\ldots\ldots + (1+r)^{N-1}]$$ (4.13)

Multiplying both sides of the above equation by (1+r), we obtain,

$$(1+r)F = A_y [(1+r) + (1+r)^2 + (1+r)^3 + \ldots\ldots\ldots + (1+r)^N]$$ (4.14)

Subtracting equation (4.13) from the equation (4.14) we get,

$$rF = A_y [(1+r)^N - 1]$$

or, $$F = \frac{A_y[(1+r)^N - 1]}{r}$$ (4.15)

4.7.2.2. Compounding for Multiple Payments in a Year

Instead of yearly income, let us consider multiple income, m is the number of income per year. Here, the yearly compound rate can be considered for monthly as r/m. The resulting formula for monthly income series is:

$$F \times (r/m) = A_m [(1+r/m)^{Nm} - 1]$$ (4.16)

where, A_m is the uniform monthly income.

4.7.2.3. Uniform Yearly and Monthly Deposit for a Future Amount

From the equation (4.15), we obtain,

$$A_y = \frac{F \times r}{(1+r)^N - 1}$$ (4.17)

For uniform monthly accumulation, from the equation (4.16), we obtain,

$$A_m = \frac{F \times (r/m)}{(1+r/m)^{Nm} - 1} .$$ (4.18)

Where, m is the number of months in the year (i.e. 12).

4.7.3. Discrete Non-Uniform Annual Cash-Flow

In practical situation, the annual cost or benefit may not equal, and the cost or benefit may not exist in every year. For example, consider the case described below:

	Money comes or goes ($) for the year			
Year	1	2	3	4
Income	1000	5000	0	2000
Cost	4000	0	500	0

In such case, we have to find out net benefit for each year and then have to convert them in future value or present value as needed (by compounding or discounting, respectively) with the single income formula, and then sum up for total value.

4.8. OTHER FACTORS TO BE CONSIDERED IN FINANCIAL STATEMENT

4.8.1. Qualitative Attributes

Since there are almost always some things that can't be quantified or given monetary values, it is important that your report include some discussion of these issues. A frank description of some of these qualitative issues in your report can help round out your conclusions, and reduce the chances of your study being used inappropriately.

4.8.2. Sensitivity Analysis

This step involves identifying the assumptions behind your cost estimates, and considering how critical they are to your calculations. If one of your assumptions turns out not to be accurate, or if conditions change during the time of your study (for example, the minimum wage goes up, affecting salary costs), will that change your whole conclusion, or is the effect strong enough that there is some leeway?

4.9. APPLICATION OF COMPOUNDING FORMULA FOR INTEREST CALCULATION

Compounding interest

If the interest of the Bank is compounding (i.e. interest on the "accumulated interest", in addition to interest on the "Capital amount"), then future accumulated amount can be calculated using the formula:

$F = P(1+r)^N$

where N is the number of years for which it is compounded, P is the starting Capital, r is the interest rate.

Simple interest

If the interest of the Bank is simple, that is not compounding (i.e. interest on the "Initial Capital" only), then the future accumulated amount can be calculated using the formula:

Future accumulated amount = Capital + Interest on capital

i.e. $F = P + (P \times r \times N)$
$\quad = P(1 + r \times N)$

4.10. WORKOUT PROBLEMS

Example 4.1.

Determine NPV and BCR of the project given below. Assume that discount rate is 8%.

Project cash flow

Year	0	1	2	3	4	5	6
Cost ($)	25000	500	500	500	500	500	1000
Revenue ($)	0	7000	10000	10000	7000	4000	4000

Salvage value at year 6, = 3000 $

Solution:

Total revenue at year 6 = revenue + salvage value
= 4000 + 3000 = 7000

Net revenue *or* income (for a particular year) = total revenue - total cost
Present value (of cost *or* revenue *or* net revenue) for a particular year is calculated as:

$$P = \frac{F}{(1 + r)^N}$$

where F = future value
$\quad$ r = discount rate
$\quad$ N = year, for which the present value is to be calculated

The calculations are summarized below:

Year	0	1	2	3	4	5	6
Cost ($)	25000	500	500	500	500	500	1000
Rev. ($)	0	7000	10000	10000	7000	4000	7000
PV of cost ($)	25000	463.0	428.7	396.9	367.5	340.3	630.2
PV of Rev. ($)	0	6481.5	8573.4	7938.3	5145.2	2722.3	2520.7

As a sample calculation, Present value of cost for year four (4)

$$= 500 / (1+0.08)^4 = 367.5$$

Sum of PV of cost = 25000.0 + 463.0 + 428.7 + 396.9 + 367.5 + 340.3+
630.2 = 27626.5

Sum of PV of revenue = 0.0 + 6481.5 + 8573.4 + 7938.3 + 5145.2 + 2722.3 + 2520.7 = 33381.4

Present value of net revenue (NPV) = Sum of PV of revenue - Sum of PV of cost = $
33381.4 - $ 27626.5
= $ 5754.9 (**Ans.**)

BCR = (Sum of PV of revenue)/(Sum of PV of cost)
= 33381.4 / 27626.5 = 1.21 (**Ans.**)

Example 4.2.

For an industrial project, the probable cost and output are given below. Find the net present value of the revenue (NPV).

Year	Cost ($)	Product unit (nos)	Unit Price ($)
0	60000	0	10
1	2000	1200	10
2	2000	1200	10
3	2000	1200	10
4	2000	1200	10
5	2000	1200	10
6	2000	1200	10
7	2000	1200	10
8	2000	1200	10
9	2000	1200	10
10	2000	1200	12
11	2000	1100	12
12	2500	1100	12
13	2500	1100	12
14	2500	1100	12
15	2500	1100	12

Soln

Revenue for a particular year = product number × unit price

Net revenue *or* income (for a particular year) = total revenue - total cost

Present value (of cost *or* revenue *or* net revenue) for a particular year is calculated as:

$$P = \frac{F}{(1+r)^N}$$

where F = future value

      r = discount rate

N = year, for which the present value is to be calculated

Sample calculation for the year 5:

Revenue = product number × unit price = 1200 × 10 = 12000

Net revenue = revenue – cost = 12000 – 2000 = 10000 $

PV of net revenue = $1000/(1+0.05)^5$ = 7835.3 $

The calculations are summarized below:

Year	Cost ($)	Product unit (nos)	Unit Price ($)	Revenue ($)	Net Rev. ($)	PV net rev. ($)
0	60000	0	10	0	-60000	-60000
1	2000	1200	10	12000	10000	9523.8
2	2000	1200	10	12000	10000	9070.3
3	2000	1200	10	12000	10000	8638.4
4	2000	1200	10	12000	10000	8227.0
5	**2000**	**1200**	**10**	**12000**	**10000**	**7835.3**
6	2000	1200	10	12000	10000	7462.2
7	2000	1200	10	12000	10000	7106.8
8	2000	1200	10	12000	10000	6768.4
9	2000	1200	10	12000	10000	6446.1
10	2000	1200	12	14400	12400	7612.5
11	2000	1100	12	13200	11200	6548.4
12	2500	1100	12	13200	10700	5958.2
13	2500	1100	12	13200	10700	5674.4
14	2500	1100	12	13200	10700	5404.2
15	2500	1100	12	13200	10700	5146.9
Sum of PV $_{net rev}$						47422.9

Thus, NPV = $ 47422.9 (Ans.)

Example 4.3.

Suppose you are an engineer with *Malaysian Department of Transportation*. You are planning about a new route from Kuala Lumpur to Kuantan to improve safety and decrease average travel time. After preliminary investigation, the information gathered is summarized in Table-4.3.

Assume that the Bank interest rate is 5%. Analyze the project, and comment on whether the project is economically justified or not.

Table 4.3. Investigation data for the route from Kuala Lumpur to Kuantan

Particulars	Value
Initial cost	$ 10 million
Annual maintenance cost	$ 0.2 million
Annual benefit to public	2 million
Expected economic life	20 yrs

Solution:

First, we have to find out the annualized value of *initial cost* (as other values are in annual basis). We know, annualized value (AV) of some present value (PV) is expressed as:

$$AV = PV \frac{i(1+i)^n}{(1+i)^n - 1}$$

Here:

  PV=   10000000

  i =   5%

  n =   20

Putting the values, AV = $ 802425. 9

Given, annual maintenance cost = $200000

Thus, total annual cost =   yearly initial cost + annual maintenance cost

  = $ 802425. 9 + $200000

  = $ 1002425.9

Given, Annual benefit = $ 2000000

Thus, BCR = Annual benefit /Annual cost

  = $ 2000000/$ 1002425.9

  = 1.995

As the BCR>1, the project is economically justified. (**Ans.**)

Examples on 'Time Value of Money' – Application of Compounding Formula

Example 4.4.

An aircraft company loaned two (02) million dollar to buy a new airbus. How much money the company will repay at the end of 5 years, if:

(a) the interest rate (simple) is 3% ?

(b) the interest rate (compound) is 3% ?

Solution

(a) For simple interest, future amount, F = P (1+ r × n)

Given:

Initial amount, P = 2000000 $
Interest rate, r = 3% = 0.03
Number of year, n = 5
Putting the values, amount to pay, F = 2000000 (1 + 0.03× 5) = 2300000 $ **(Ans.)**

(b) For compound interest, future amount, $F = F = P(1+r)^n$
$$= 2000000 (1 + 0.03)^5$$
$$= 2318548.1 \ \$ \ \textbf{(Ans.)}$$

Example 4.5.
An industry owner wants to deposit certain amount of money with a target of having a total sum of 100,000 US$ at the end of 10 years with a view to buy new machine at that time. If the bank interest rate is 5%, find:

a) What yearly deposit is required?
b) What monthly deposit is required (instead of yearly)?
c) What present deposit (one-time) is required instead of yearly or monthly deposit?
d) What amount will be accumulated after 7 yrs with the yearly deposit scheme?

Solution:
(a) We know, for uniform yearly deposit,

$$A_y = \frac{F \times r}{(1+r)^N - 1}$$

Given:
F = $ 100000
r = 5%
N = 10 years

Putting the values, we get, $A_y = \$ 7950$ **(Ans.)**

(b) For uniform monthly deposit, we know:

$$A_m = \frac{F \times (r/m)}{(1+r/m)^{Nm} - 1}$$

Here:

F = $ 100000
r = 5%
N = 10 years
m = 12 (number of split/deposit in a year)

Putting the values, we get, $A_m = \$ 644$ **(Ans.)**

(c) For single installment, we know: $F = P(1+r)^N$

Or, $P = F / (1+r)^N$

F = $ 100000

r = 5%

N = 10 years

Thus, P = $ 61391 (**Ans.**)

(d) For uniform yearly deposit, Future amount after N years:

$$F = \frac{A[(1+r)^N - 1]}{r}$$

Here:

N = 7 yrs

A = $ 7950

r = 5%

Putting the values, F_7 = $ 64732.7 (**Ans.**)

Example 4.6.

A businessman planned to deposit $5,00,000 in a Banks's deposit scheme that returns 5% per year (compounding), and planned to withdraw $20,000 at the end of each year, up to the 6th year. What amount will be available at the end of 7th year?

Solution:

We know, future amount, $F = P(1+r)^n$

Here,

Initial capital, P = $ 500000

Interest rate, r = 5%

At the end of year 1, $F = 500000 (1+ 0.05)^1 = 525000$

As withdrawal is 20000, net amount available at the end of the year = (525000 – 20000) = 505000; which is the capital for the year 2.

Similarly, other calculations are done and summarized below:

Year	Capital at the beginning of year i ($)	Total money at the end of the year ($)	Withdrawal ($)	Net amount at the end of year ($)
1	500000	525000	20000	505000
2	505000	530250	20000	510250
3	510250	535762.5	20000	515762.5
4	515762.5	541550.63	20000	521550.6
5	521550.6	547628.16	20000	527628.2
6	527628.2	554009.56	20000	534009.6
7	534009.6	**560710.04**		

Hence, the amount at 7th year = $ 560710 **(Ans.)**

Example 4.7.

An industry owner deposited $ 10,000 in a Bank at the beginning of year 2002, and then (starting at the beginning of next year) continued annually by $ 1,000. If the interest rate of the Bank is 3% (compound), what amount will be accumulated after 15 years?

Solution:

Here, two types of deposit are apparent:

(a) Fixed (one time) deposit of $ 10,000 at year 2002; and
(b) Yearly uniform deposit of $ 1000

(a) For fixed deposit
We know, $F = P(1+r)^N$
Given:
Capital, P = 10000
Interest rate, r =   3%
Time period (in year), N = 15

Putting the values, F = $ 15579.7
(b) For yearly uniform deposit

We know for uniform yearly deposit,

$$F = A \frac{(1+r)^N - 1}{r}$$

Here:

A = 1000
N = 15
r = 3%

Putting the values, F = $ 18598.9
Thus, total amount will be = $ 15579.7 + $ 18598.9 = $ 34178.6 **(Ans.)**

Example 4.8.

Your father offered you to put sufficient money into a saving account of a 'Bank' to generate your educational expenses. If the account offers:
a) 4% interest per year, what minimum amount should be deposited so that you can get $9,600 at the end of each year?
b) monthly interest of 0.03%, what minimum amount should be deposited to get $800 at the end of each month?

Solution:
(a) We know, F = P(1+r)N
For N=1, F = P(1+r) = P + Pr

That is, Future (total) amount = capital + interest on capital
As the objective of the stated "deposit" is to generate desired amount (RM 9600 per year), but not to exploit the capital (P), interest for each year (i.e. P× r) must be equal to RM 9600.

That is, P × r = 9600

Thus, P = 9600/ 0.04 [given, r = 4% = 0.04]
= 240000

That is, minimum deposit amount to get the above req. amount = $ 240000 (**Ans.**)

(b) For the given condition, Monthly interest must be equal to $ 800
i.e., P × r = 800
Given, r = 0.03%
Thus, P = 800/ 0.03
= $ 2666667 (**Ans.**)

Exercise

4.1 What is the importance of economic and financial analysis in developing engineering projects?

4.2 Write short notes on: NPV, NFV, cost effectiveness, least cost analysis, nominal and real value, discounting, compounding, annualized value.

4.3 What is NPV curve? What are the steps in NPV analysis?

4.4 Derive the equation for net present value analysis:

$$NPV = NB_0 + \sum_{t=1}^{n} \frac{NB_t}{(1+r)^t}$$

where, r is the interest rate, t is the time period in year.

4.5 Calculate NPV and BCR of the Project-A and Project-B given below. Assume, discount rate is 10 % and no salvage value at the end of the projects.

Project-A

	Year			
	0	1	4	6
Cost ($)	12000	700	600	900
Revenue ($)	0	8000	12000	5000

Project-B

	Year			
	0	1	5	7
Cost ($)	20000	5000	1000	1000
Revenue ($)	0	10000	20000	10000

4.6 Calculate NPV and BCR of the cash flow of an industrial project, details of which are given below. Assume discount rate of 6%.

Year	0	1	3	5	7	9	11	13	15	17	19
Cost ($)	60000	5000	1000	1000	1000	1000	1000	1000	1000	1000	1500
Product unit (nos)	0	1600	1600	1600	1600	1600	1600	1600	1600	1600	1600
Unit price of product,$		8	8	8	8	8	8	8	8	10	10

4.7 'Mr. John Mitchel' borrowed $2,000 from 'CIMB Bank' to buy a Motor cycle. Calculate the total due after 03 years, if the bank charges:

(a) 4% interest (simple/non-compounding),
(b) 4% interest (compounding).

4.8 'Mr. Aminur Rahman deposited $20,000 in the Bank 2 years ago, with an interest rate (compound) of 8% per annum. Calculate the total amount accumulated now.

4.9 A student wants to deposit certain amount (in one installment) in a 'Bank' to get US$50,000 after 04 years. If the Bank offers 4% benefit per year (compound), what amount should the student be deposited?

4.10 An aircraft company loaned 3 million dollar to buy a new airbus. How much money the company will repay at the end of 6 years, if the interest rate is:

(a) 5% (simple)?
(b) 5 % (compound)?

4.11 A businessman planned to deposit $7,00,000 in a Banks's deposit scheme that returns 4.5% per year (compound), and planned to withdraw $21,000 at the end of each year, up to the 6th year. What amount will be available at the end of 8th year?

4.12 Your father offered you to put sufficient money into a saving account of 'Bank Islam' to generate your educational expenses, which is equivalent to US$10,000 per year. If the account offers 3% benefit per year,

a) What minimum amount should be deposited so that you can get US$10,000 at the end of each year ?
b) If the Bank offers monthly interest of 0.03%, what minimum amount should be deposited to get US$850 at the end of each month?

Chapter 5

INDICATORS AND DECISION RULES FOR PROJECT SELECTION AMONG ALTERNATIVES

5.1. INDICATORS FOR PROJECT JUDGMENT

5.1.1. Concept and Types

We are interested in such a project that will yield a greater output for national economy. A test of economic viability needs to be applied for single project as well as multiple options. The following indicators are normally used to compare the project alternatives:

1. Net present value (NPV)
2. Economic internal rate of return (IRR)
3. Benefit-cost ratio (BCR)

Under certain circumstances, 'Payback period' is also used.

5.1.2 Comparative Merits and Demerits of the Indicators

The IRR is a rate or ratio, not an amount, thus more useful for comparing unlike/dissimilar investments. It is also useful for making comparisons between different sized farms and between different periods, and international comparisons. However, IRR calculation requires cash inflow as well as cash outflow.

The NPV is suitable for absolute measure of value of an inflow-outflow system. The NPV is well accepted for sound reasons, but it has limitations. To solve for NPV, one must first calculate the opportunity cost of the capital, also called 'discount rate'. The rate is used to calculate NPV. The NPV is highly sensitive to the discounting rate. Using different discounting rates can change NPV ranking, and therefore not very useful for comparisons between organizations – especially those of different sizes projects.

Both IRR and NPV are widely used to decide which investment(s) to undertake and which investment(s) not to make. The aim is to maximize the total NPV, but not to IRR. The major difference between IRR and NPV is that while NPV is expressed in monetary units (Dollar, for example), the IRR is the true benefit (interest) rate expected from an investment expressed as a percentage. It does not tell us about the total income from the project alternatives; thus not suitable to compare different sized projects, and mutually exclusive projects. At the same IRR (or even at lower IRR), the total income from a large project may be much higher than that of a small project.

The BCR is a direct indicator of benefit (gain) or loss from a project (BCR = total benefit / total cost, BCR>1.0 indicates gain, BCR<1.0 indicates loss). Similar to IRR, it does not tell us about the total income from the project alternatives; thus not suitable to compare different sized projects and mutually exclusive projects. At the same BCR (or even at lower BCR), the total income from a large project may be much higher than that of a small project.

'Payback Period'(time required to recover the capital) suffers from several flaws: it does not consider all of the project's cash-flows, there is no generalized formula for all types of cash-flow (regular/periodic, uniform/non-uniform), the accept/reject criterion is arbitrary.

In summary, it can be said that the BCR and IRR give identical signal, and hence have essentially equivalent utility. The two measures complement each other. The NPV is a better absolute measure, where IRR and BCR are better relative measure.

When a single indicator is used, the NPV and IRR can rank the alternatives differently. The BCR, IRR and NPV together can give a better picture of the problem than either alone.

5.2. DETERMINATION OF THE INDICATORS

Procedure for determining the NPV, BCR and 'Payback period' has been described in earlier Chapters (BCR in Chapter-2, NPV and 'Payback period' in Chapter-4). The internal rate of return (IRR) is the discount rate for which the NPV of the project cash flow is zero. It is determined by trial, determining NPV at different discount rate, as of Figure given below (Figure 5.1). It can easily be done in Microsoft Excel.

The curve crosses the horizontal line (indicating NPV = 0) between 0.04 and 0.06. So the internal rate of return is between 0.04 and 0.06 (nearly at 0.05). Thus, the internal rate of return (IRR) is 0.05.

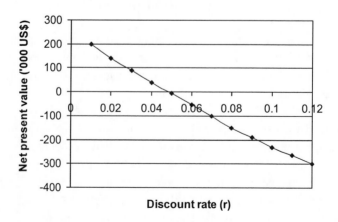

Figure 5.1. Trial for determining IRR.

5.3. SELECTION CRITERIA

5.3.1. Mutually Independent Projects

'Mutually Independent projects' are those projects which (any one) can be selected without any restriction on the others.

Essential selection criteria:
- the BCR should be greater than unity
- the NPV should be positive

Selection procedure:
At first, choose the project which has the highest BCR and/or IRR. If fund *or* capital is still available, select second project which has second highest BCR and/or IRR. Then, until capital is available, select projects sequentially (from higher to lower BCR) having BCR>1 and NPV>0.

5.3.2. Mutually Exclusive Projects

'Mutually exclusive projects' are those projects from which any one project can be selected with sacrificing of the others (that is, only one can be selected).
Essential criteria:

- the BCR should be greater than unity
- the NPV should be positive

Selection procedure:
Choose the project having highest NPV.

5.3.2. Decision Rule for 'Payback Period'

As mentioned earlier, the accept/reject criterion of 'Payback period, P_p' is something arbitrary. Two conditions can be considered:

(A) If the priority is to get return (payback) the capital quickly, but not the rate *or* total return/profit; then:
   (1) For mutually independent project
      At first, choose the project having lowest 'Payback period'. Then sequentially choose the projects having P_p less than a specified number of years (arbitrary, to be chosen by the decision maker / project owner).
   (2) For mutually exclusive project
      Choose the project having lowest 'Payback period'.

(B) If the decision maker (project owner) wants to optimize among return rate (or BCR), total return/profit, and 'Payback period'; no generalized rule can be set for that purpose. Rather, the decision maker have to choose by his own judgment (keeping in mind his priority aspect).

5.4. Other Considerations for "Governmental (Public)" and "Private" Investment/Project

5.4.1. Public Project

The factors affecting decision making process are described in Chapter 1. The normal economic criteria are applicable for "Public" or "Governmental" projects or investments.

Other factors such as governmental/public priority, employment generation, future well-being of the citizen, self-sufficiency of the basic needs, etc. should be taken into account. Even a project is not financially profitable (for example - basic need of the people, such as drinking water supply), it should be implemented for the interest of the citizen.

5.4.2. Private or Personal Project

For 'personal' or 'private' (including business groups) investments, some other factors need to be considered in addition to the above criteria. The factors are:

(a) Cost of capital

'Personal' or 'private' money may be borrowed *or* loaned from Bank or other financial organization/institution, and they will charge a *'fee'* or *'a return rate'* or *'an interest'*. So, the rate of return from the proposed project must be greater than the 'fee' or 'interest of the capital' (termed as *cost of capital*).

(b) Risk of return

If there is a risk to get output from a project, the expected (or desired) rate of return from the project is higher. The higher the risk, the higher the rate of return should be. For example, the business add more profit for 'green vegetable' items than the 'cloth or other non-rotten' items due to risk (and sometimes some items are really rotten). This higher value is the cost (or value) of risk.

(c) Return rate from safe investment

The money (capital) can be deposited in safe scheme such as Bank, and it will generate money (in the form of interest). The interest rate *or* return rate can be compared with the return rate of the proposed project (IRR), whether the IRR is greater than the *'safe return rate*' or not. The IRR should be greater than the *safe return rate* for attraction of "private" investment.

Considering the above points, a term '*minimum attractive rate of return*' (MARR) is introduced to qualify the 'private' investment. It must be greater than the 'cost of capital' or 'return rate from safe investment' and should include 'cost of risk', if there is any risk associated with the project. Schematically, it can be shown as of Figure 5.2.

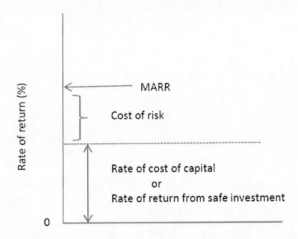

Figure 5.2. Schematic representation of minimum attractive rate of return (MARR).

The MARR is the return rate at which the private investors will be willing to invest in project under the prevailing conditions of cost of capital, safe rate of return, and investment risk. It is not a fixed rate or value, but will vary depending on the circumstances; and the financial manager/analyst will decide its value. In mathematical relation, it can be expressed as:

IRR ≥ MARR > ('cost of capital' or 'safe return rate' + 'cost of risk, if any')
Between the 'cost of capital' or 'safe return rate', the higher one should be used.

5.5. WORKOUT PROBLEMS

Examples on Project justification /Selection among alternatives

Example 5.1.
An aircraft company is considering two alternatives for buying a new air-bus. The most likely cash flow for the two alternatives is as follows:

	First cost ($)	Annual operating cost ($)	Annual revenue ($)	Salvage value ($)	Economic life (yr)
Model – A	180,000	20,000	45,000	25,000	10
Model – B	200,000	18,000	55,000	30,000	12

Which aircraft should the company buy?

Solution

We know, annualized value of a present value (cost or revenue), $A = P\left(\dfrac{i(1+i)^N}{(1+i)^N - 1}\right)$,

where P is the present value, i is the interest rate, N is the service life or economic life.

Model-A

Annualized value of first cost = 22192.4

Total revenue at the last year of economic life (year 10) = Ann. Rev. + salvage value = 70,000

The whole calculations are summarized below:

Year	Annualized value of first cost	Annual operating cost	Total cost	Revenue	Net revenue	Present value (PV) of net revenue
1	22192.4	20,000	42192.4	45,000	2807.6	2699.6
2	22192.4	20,000	42192.4	45,000	2807.6	2595.8
3	22192.4	20,000	42192.4	45,000	2807.6	2496.0
4	22192.4	20,000	42192.4	45,000	2807.6	2400.0
5	22192.4	20,000	42192.4	45,000	2807.6	2307.7
6	22192.4	20,000	42192.4	45,000	2807.6	2218.9
7	22192.4	20,000	42192.4	45,000	2807.6	2133.6
8	22192.4	20,000	42192.4	45,000	2807.6	2051.5
9	22192.4	20,000	42192.4	45,000	2807.6	1972.6
10	22192.4	20,000	42192.4	45,000	2807.6	1896.7
Sum						22772

Model-B

Annualized value of first cost = 21310.4

Total revenue at the last year of economic life (year 12) = Ann. Rev. + salvage value = 85,000

The whole calculations are summarized below:

Year	Annualized value of first cost	Annual operating cost	Total cost	Revenue	Net revenue	Present value (PV) of net revenue
1	21310.4	18,000	39310.4	55,000	15689.6	15086.1
2	21310.4	18,000	39310.4	55,000	15689.6	14505.9
3	21310.4	18,000	39310.4	55,000	15689.6	13948.0
4	21310.4	18,000	39310.4	55,000	15689.6	13411.5
5	21310.4	18,000	39310.4	55,000	15689.6	12895.7
6	21310.4	18,000	39310.4	55,000	15689.6	12399.7
7	21310.4	18,000	39310.4	55,000	15689.6	11922.8
8	21310.4	18,000	39310.4	55,000	15689.6	11464.2
9	21310.4	18,000	39310.4	55,000	15689.6	11023.3
10	21310.4	18,000	39310.4	55,000	15689.6	10599.3
11	21310.4	18,000	39310.4	55,000	15689.6	10191.6
12	21310.4	18,000	39310.4	85,000	45689.6	28537.6
Sum						165985.6

From the above calculation, it is observed that, NPV of Model-B > NPV of Model-A. Therefore, Model-B aircraft should buy. (**Ans.**)

Example 5.2.

Perform financial and economic analyses of the given projects to justify the investment and suggest the best project option, when they are:

(a) Mutually independent,
(b) Mutually exclusive.

Assume discount rate of 10 %.

Project-A

Year	0	1	2	3	4	5
Cost ($)	50000	5000	5000	5000	5000	5000
Revenue ($)	0	10000	40000	40000	30000	20000

Project-B

Year	0	1	2	4	6
Cost ($)	50000	7000	1000	1000	2000
Revenue ($)	0	25000	50000	30000	25000

Project-C

Year	0	1	2	3
Cost ($)	100000	5000	5000	5000
Revenue ($)	0	80000	70000	60000

Solution

For comparison of multiple projects, we have to determine NPV (of net revenue), BCR, and IRR.

Analysis for project-A

Net revenue = revenue − cost

Present value (PV, at year zero) of net revenue for year N,

$PV_N = F/(1+r)^N$, where r is the discount rate (here, 10% , given).

For example, PV of 'net revenue' for the year 3, $PV_3 = 35000/(1+0.1)^3$
  = 26296.0

Similarly, PV of cost and PV of revenue are calculated separately, to find BCR. The calculated results are summarized below:

Year	0	1	2	3	4	5
Cost ($)	50000	5000	5000	5000	5000	5000
Revenue ($)	0	10000	40000	40000	30000	20000
Net revenue ($)	-50000	5000	35000	35000	25000	15000
PV of net revenue (for year N), $	-50000	4545.5	28925.6	26296.0	17075.3	9313.8
PV cost for year N), $	50000	4545.5	4132.2	3756.6	3415.1	3104.6
PV revenue (for year N), $	0	9090.9	33057.9	30052.6	20490.4	12418.4

Sum of $PV_{net-rev}$ (NPV) = -50000 + 4545.5 + 28925.6 + 26296.0 +
+ 17075.3 + 9313.8 = 36156

Sum of PV_{cost} = 50000 + 4545.5+ 4132.2+ 3756.6 + 3415.1 + 3104.6
= 68953.9

Sum of $PV_{revenue}$ = 0+ 9090.9 + 33057.9 + 30052.6 + 20490.4 + 12418.4
= 105110.2
BCR = (Sum of $PV_{revenue}$)/(sum of PV_{cost}) = 105110.2 / 68953.9 = **1.52**

Determination of IRR

For determination of IRR, NPV is determined for different discount rates, to find the discount rate for which NPV is zero.

The NPVs for different r are summarized below:

r (%)	NPV
0.1	36156
15	25577
25	9475
30	3280
33	17
33.05	-35
33.02	-4

Thus, IRR ≈ 33.02 %
Analysis for project-B

Year	0	1	2	4	6
Cost ($)	50000	7000	1000	1000	2000
Revenue ($)	0	25000	50000	30000	25000
Net revenue ($)	-50000	18000	49000	29000	23000
PV of net revenue (for year N), $	-50000	16363.6	40495.9	19807.4	12982.9
PV cost (for year N), $	50000	6363.6	826.4	683.0	1128.9
PV revenue (for year N), $	0	22727.3	41322.3	20490.4	14111.8

Sum of $PV_{net\text{-}rev}$ (NPV) = -50000 + 16363.6 + 40495.9 + 19807.4
+ 12982.9 = **39650**

Sum of PV_{cost} = 50000 + 6363.6 + 826.4 + 683.0 + 1128.9 = 59002.0

Sum of $PV_{revenue}$ = 0+ 22727.3+ 41322.3+ 20490.4+ 14111.8 = 98651.8

BCR = (Sum of $PV_{revenue}$) /(sum of PV_{cost}) = 98651.8 / 59002.0 = **1.67**

Determination of IRR

For determination of IRR, NPV is determined for different discount rates, to find the discount rate for which NPV is zero.

The NPVs for different r are summarized below:

r (%)	NPV
10	39650
35	2750
40	-1539
37	956
37.5	525
38	100
38.1	15
38.12	-1

The NPV is zero at r ≈ 38.12 %.
Thus, the IRR = **38.12 %.**

Analysis for project-C

Year	0	1	2	3
Cost ($)	100000	5000	5000	5000
Revenue ($)	0	80000	70000	60000
Net revenue ($)	-100000	75000	65000	55000
PV of net revenue (for year N), $	-100000	68181.8	53719.0	41322.3
PV cost (for year N), $	100000	4545.5	4132.2	3756.6
PV reven. (for year N), $	0	72727.3	57851.2	45078.9

Sum of $PV_{net\text{-}rev}$ (NPV) = -100000 + 68181.8 + 53719.0 + 41322.3
= **63223**
Sum of PV_{cost} = 100000 + 4545.5 + 4132.2 + 3756.6 = 112434

Sum of $PV_{revenue}$ = 0 + 72727.3 +   57851.2 + 45078.9 = 175657

BCR = (Sum of $PV_{revenue}$) /(sum of PV_{cost}) =175657/112434 = **1.56**

Determination of IRR

The NPVs for different r are summarized below:

r (%)	NPV
10	63223
30	21188
40	6778
50	-4815
45	681
45.2	450
45.6	-9
45.59	3

The NPV is zero (0) when r ≈ 45.59.
Thus, the IRR is 45.59%.

Comparison of the projects and selection

The summary of NPV, BCR, and IRR are as follows:

	NPV	BCR	IRR	Duration of project (year)
Project-A	36,156	1.52	33.02	5
Project-B	39,650	1.67	38.12	6
Project-C	63,223	1.56	45.59	3

All the projects produce NPV greater than zero and BCR greater than one, hence qualify financial criteria.

(a) When the projects are mutually independent

From the calculation, it is observed that the Project-C generates the highest economic rate of return (IRR), but the Project-B scores the highest BCR. Under this circumstance, we have to consider several aspects. First, duration of the project, second, the comparison of BCR, and third, risks associated with the projects. The Project-C is much more short duration (half of that of B) than the Project-B, thus facilitates the repetition of the same project. In case of BCR, the BCR of Project-C is comparable with that of Project-B. If risks are similar for both the Projects, Project-C may be implemented first at maximum possible numbers (up to which the prevailing condition permits). After that, if money/fund is available, Project-B should be implemented at maximum possible numbers (up to which the prevailing condition permits).

Last of all, if fund is available, Project-A may be implemented.

(b) when the projects are mutually exclusive

The Project-C generates the highest NPV among the projects. So, the Project-C should be implemented.

In case, the available capital/fund does not allow to implement the Project-C, the Project-B should be implemented (as it generates the 2nd highest NPV).

If the available capital does not allow to implement the Project-B, then Project-A should be implemented.

Example 5.3.

A flood mitigation reservoir has been proposed near Kuala Lampur, Malaysia. The initial cost of construction is estimated as 1×10^6 US$. The operating and maintenance cost is expected to about 5,000 US$ per year.

Expected benefit from 'prevention of flood damage' is about 1.2×10^4 US$ per year. Assume that no major dragging will be necessary within 25 years (that is effective life is 25 years). Is the project economically justifiable?

Solution

Assume discount rate, r = 6%

Total cost for a year = construction cost + maintenance and operational cost

Net benefit = benefit – cost

Present value of "net benefit" for a particular year, $P = F/(1+r)^N$

The calculations are summarized below:

NPV (of benefit) = -910516.5

Since the NPV is negative, the project is not justified economically. (**Ans.**)

Yr	Construction cost (US$)	Maintenance and Operation cost (US$)	Total cost (US$)	Benefit (US$)	Net benefit (US$)	PV of net benefit for yr i (US$)
0	1.00E+06	0	1000000	0	-1000000	-1000000
1		5000	5000	12000	7000	6603.8
2		5000	5000	12000	7000	6230.0
3		5000	5000	12000	7000	5877.3
4		5000	5000	12000	7000	5544.7
5		5000	5000	12000	7000	5230.8
6		5000	5000	12000	7000	4934.7
7		5000	5000	12000	7000	4655.4
8		5000	5000	12000	7000	4391.9
9		5000	5000	12000	7000	4143.3
10		5000	5000	12000	7000	3908.8
11		5000	5000	12000	7000	3687.5
12		5000	5000	12000	7000	3478.8
13		5000	5000	12000	7000	3281.9
14		5000	5000	12000	7000	3096.1
15		5000	5000	12000	7000	2920.9

(Continued)

Yr	Construction cost (US$)	Maintenance and Operation cost (US$)	Total cost (US$)	Benefit (US$)	Net benefit (US$)	PV of net benefit for yr i (US$)
16		5000	5000	12000	7000	2755.5
17		5000	5000	12000	7000	2599.6
18		5000	5000	12000	7000	2452.4
19		5000	5000	12000	7000	2313.6
20		5000	5000	12000	7000	2182.6
21		5000	5000	12000	7000	2059.1
22		5000	5000	12000	7000	1942.5
23		5000	5000	12000	7000	1832.6
24		5000	5000	12000	7000	1728.8
25		5000	5000	12000	7000	1631.0
Sum						-910516.5

Example 5.4.

In 'North China Plain Area' of China, the estimated cost of a Drainage Project is US$ 62,000 (at the beginning of the project). The effective life of the project is expected to 20 years. The interest on capital is 7%. The annualized value of the operation and maintenance cost is 3% of the initial cost. The salvage value from the project is US$5000 at the end of the project. The annualized value of the benefit from the project is US$ 12,430. Is the project economically viable?

Solution
Given:
Initial cost = 62000 US$
Effective life = 20 yrs
Interest rate = 7%
Annual. Opera. Cost = 3% of initial cost
Salvage value at yr 20 =   5000 US$
Annual. benefit = 12430 US$

We know, annualized value, $A = \dfrac{F \times r}{(1+r)^N - 1}$ (i)

Putting the values, Annualized value of initial cost = 5852.36 US$

Annualized ope. and mainte. cost =   (3/100)× 62000 = 1860 US$
Total annual cost = 5852.36 US$ + 1860 US$ = 7712.36 US$
Present value of the salvage price = 1292.1 US$ [by, P = F/(1+r)^N]
Annualized value of salvage price = 122.0 US$ [by eqn. (i)]

Total annual benefit = Annu.benifit + Annu. Salvage = 12430 US$ +
+ 122.0 US$ = 12552.0 US$

BCR =(Total annual benefit) / (Total annual cost)
= 12552.0 US$ / 7712.36 US$ = 1.628

As the BCR>1.0, the project is justified. (**Ans.**)

Example 5.5.

An irrigation development project has been planned in an area. The tentative cash-flow from the project considering is given below. Test the economic viability of the project. Assume discount rate of 5%.

Cash-flow:

Year	Initial cost ($)	Operation cost ($)	Maintenance cost ($)	Revenue ($)
0	50,000	500		10000
1		500		10000
2		500		10000
3		500		10000
4		500	300	10000
5		500		10000
6		550		10000
7		550		10000
8		550		10000
9		550		10000
10		550	1000	10000
11		550		12000
12		550		12000
13		600		12000
14		600		12000
15		600	1000	12000
16		600		13000
17		600		13000
18		600		13000
19		600	400	13000
20		600		13000

Solution

Total cost for a year = Operation cost + Maintenance cost
(For the starting year (zero year), only the initial cost)

Net revenue = total revenue – total cost

Present value of "net revenue" for year N, $P = F/(1+r)^N$
For sample illustration, present value (PV) of 'net revenue' for year 5,
$P_5 = 9500/(1+0.05)^5 = 7443.5$

The results are summarized as follows.

Year	Total cost ($)	Net revenue ($)	PV of net revenue ($)
0	50,500	- 40,500	- 40500
1	500	9,500	9047.6
2	500	9,500	8616.8
3	500	9,500	8206.5
4	800	9,200	7568.9
5	500	9,500	7443.5
6	550	9,450	7051.7
7	550	9,450	6715.9
8	550	9,450	6396.1
9	550	9,450	6091.6
10	1,550	8,450	5187.6
11	550	11,450	6694.6
12	550	11,450	6375.8
13	600	11,400	6045.7
14	600	11,400	5757.8
15	1,600	10,400	5002.6
16	600	12,400	5680.6
17	600	12,400	5410.1
18	600	12,400	5152.5
19	1,000	12,000	4748.8
20	600	12,400	4673.4
		NPV =	**87367.9**

The present value of the net revenue is greater than zero (87367.9>0), thus the project is economically justified. (**Ans.**)

Examples on MARR

Example 5.6.
What would be the minimum attractive rate of return for an investment, if the cost of capital is 4%, safe return rate is 3%, and cost of risk is 1%.

Solution:
Cost of capital = 4%,
Safe return rate = 3% (< capital cost)
Cost of risk = 1%
Total of (cost of capital + cost of risk) = 4% + 1% = 5 %
MARR should be >5 %, say 6%. (Ans.)

Example 5.7.

Find out the minimum attractive rate of return for the following investment plan:

- the cost of capital is 5%,
- safe return rate is 6%,
- no cost for risk

Solution

Between the cost of capital (5%) and safe return rate (6%), the safe return rate is higher. As there is no cost for risk, the MARR should be greater than 6%.

Thus, we can take MARR as 7%. (Ans.)

Example 5.8.

Determine the economic rate of return for an investment of "Samsung Groups of Industries", from the following cash-flow of the project:

Year	0	1	2	3	4	5
Cost	5000	500	0	0	500	0
Revenue	0	1000	1000	4000	1000	2000

Solution

By trial and error, assuming different discount rate (r), the NPV is calculated, and summarized below. For sample r ($r = 0.08$), the NPV analysis is shown.

Taking r = 0.08,

Year	0	1	2	3	4	5
Cost ($)	5000	500	0	0	500	0
Rev. ($)	0	1000	1000	4000	1000	2000
Income =	-5000	500	1000	4000	500	2000
NPV of income for the year	-5000	463	857	3175	368	1361
Sum of NPV =		1224				

NPV for different discount rate:

Discount rate	0.01	0.03	0.05	0.06	0.07	0.08	0.14	0.16	0.155
NPV	2741	2258	1817	1611	1413	1224	243	-35	33

NPV is zero at about discount rate 0.157.

Thus, the IRR = 0.157 *or* 15.7% (**Ans.**)

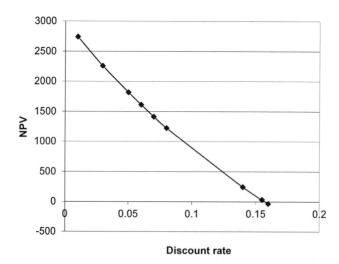

Example 5.9.

A project is planned by "Bashundhara Group of Industries" to implement, and the tentative cash-flow of the proposed project is given below. The management of the company wants at least 10 % return per year from the project. From the financial analysis, comment on the justification of the project.

Cash-flow of the project:

Year	0	1	3	5
Cash outflow	40000	0	0	0
Cash inflow	0	0	0	80000

Solution

Given: Minimum required rate of return (i.e. MARR) = 10%

Net cash-flow of the project is given below. Net cash-flow = cash inflow – cash outflow

Year	0	1	3	5
Cash outflow	40000	0	0	0
Cash inflow	0	0	0	80000
Net cash-flow	-40000	0	0	80000

We have to find out the IRR by trial and error:

r value	P-5	NPV
5%	62682.1	22682.1
10%	49673.7	9673.7
15%	39774.1	-225.9
14%	41549.5	1549.5
14.87%	39999.7	-0.3

Thus, the IRR ≈ 14.87%, which is greater than the minimum expected return rate (10%).

Hence, the proposed project is justified. **(Ans)**

Example 5.10.

A proposed wind-energy farm is expected to installment cost of $50,000. This is expected to save $6,000 per year for 12 yrs in electricity cost and $20,000 at the end of 12 yrs in equipment refurbishment/upgrading cost.

(a) Find out the rate of return from the project.

(b) Is the project economically viable if MARR is 10% ?

Solution

(a) By trial and error, assuming different discount rate (r), the NPV is calculated, and summarized below.

r	NPV
0.04	18802
0.06	10242
0.08	3159
0.09	75
0.1	2745
0.091	-218
0.0903	-13

The NPV calculation for r = 0.0902 is given below:

yr	Cost	Rev.	Net Rev.	PV of Net Rev.for yr i
0	50000		-50000	-50000
1		6000	6000	5503.6
2		6000	6000	5048.2
3		6000	6000	4630.6
4		6000	6000	4247.4
5		6000	6000	3896.0
6		6000	6000	3573.7
7		6000	6000	3278.0
8		6000	6000	3006.8
9		6000	6000	2758.0
10		6000	6000	2529.8
11		6000	6000	2320.5
12		26000	26000	9223.6
			NPV =	16

The NPV is zero for r ≈ 0.09025.

Thus, the rate of return (IRR) is 9.025 %. **(Ans.)**

(b) As the calculated rate of return is less than the desired MARR (9.025% <10 %), the project is not acceptable (not viable in this case). **(Ans.)**

Example 5.11.

Calculate the *Payback period* for the following project:

Year	0	1	2	3	4	5
DNCF	-2000	500	1000	400	300	1000

DNCF = Discounted net cash-flow

Soln

For regular cash-flow,

P_p = (Last year with a negative ' Discounted cumulative net cash-flow') + (Absolute value of net cash-flow in that year)/(Net cash-flow in the preceding year)

Year	0	1	2	3	4	5
DNCF	-2000	500	1000	400	300	1000
Cu. DNCF	-2000	-1500	-500	-100	200	1200

Cu. = Cumulative

Thus, P_p = 3 + (100/300) = 3.33 year (**Ans.**)

Example 5.12

Calculate the *Payback period* for the following project:

Year	0	1	3	5	7	10
DNCF	-5000	500	500	2000	1000	6000

DNCF = Discounted net cash-flow

Soln

For irregular cash-flow, 'Payback Period' is the "First year with a positive *Cumulative discounted net cash-flow*".

Year	0	1	3	5	7	10
DNCF	-5000	500	500	2000	1000	6000
Cu.DNCF	-5000	-4500	-4000	-2000	-1000	5000

From the calculated data, 'Pacyback period' = 10 years (**Ans.**)

Exercise

5.1 What are the indicators commonly used for project judgment/selection?

5.2 Discuss merits and demerits of different indicators.

5.3 Describe the procedure for determining different indicators.

5.4 Discuss the considerations for "Governmental (public)" and "Private" investment/ project.

5.5 What is attractive rate of return (MARR)? Show the MARR in graph.

5.6 What would be the minimum attractive rate of return for an investment, if the cost of capital is 3.5%, safe return rate is 4%, and cost of risk is 1.5%.

5.7 Find out the minimum attractive rate of return for the following investment plan:
- the cost of capital is 4%,
- safe return rate is 6%,
- no cost for risk

5.8 Determine the economic rate of return for an investment of "Sinhoa Groups of Industries", from the following cash-flow of the project:

Year	0	1	3	5	7	9
Cost	50000	5000	0	1000	1500	1000
Revenue	0	10000	10000	40000	10000	20000

5.9 A project is planned by "Jamuna Group of Industries" to implement, and the tentative cash-flow of the proposed project is given below. The management of the company wants at least 12 % return per year from the project. From the financial analysis, comment on the justification of the project.

Cash-flow of the project:

Year	0	1	3	6
Cash outflow ($)	50,000	0	0	0
Cash inflow ($)	0	10000	20000	80000

5.10 A proposed Solar-energy farm is expected to installment cost of $30,000. This is expected to save $5,000 per year for 15 yrs in electricity cost and $15,000 at the end of 15 yrs in equipment refurbishment/upgrading cost.

(a) Find out the rate of return from the project.

(b) Is the project economically viable if MARR is 11%?

5.11 A manufacturing company is considering to buy a new machine. They have two alternatives (two models) for selection. The most likely cash flow for the two alternatives is as follows:

	First cost ($)	Annual operating cost ($)	Annual revenue ($)	Salvage value ($)	Economic life (yr)
Model – 1	80,000	15,000	35,000	15,000	8
Model – 2	100,000	12,000	45,000	18,000	10

Which machine should the company buy?

5.12. An investor is investing $20,000 today. If he receives $6000, 15000, and 16000 after 2, 3, and 4 year respectively, what is the rate of return?

5.13 Perform economic and financial analysis of the given projects to justify the investment and suggest the best project option, when they are:

(a) Mutually independent,
(b) Mutually exclusive.

Assume discount rate of 6 %.

Project-A

Year	0	1	2	3	4	5
Cost ($)	70000	5000	15000	5000	10000	5000
Revenue ($)	0	12000	35000	25000	20000	25000

Salvage value at year 5 is $ 6000.

Project-B

Year	0	1	3	5	7
Cost ($)	55000	8000	1000	2000	2000
Revenue ($)	0	27000	45000	28000	22000

No salvage value.

Project-C

Year	0	1	2	3	5
Cost ($)	120000	5000	5000	5000	4000
Revenue ($)	0	68000	70000	60000	40000

No salvage value.

Chapter 6

RISKS AND UNCERTAINTIES IN ENGINEERING PROJECTS

6.1. BACKGROUND AND PERSPECTIVES

In evaluating capital budgeting decisions, quantitative approaches (e.g. traditional discounted cash flow and real options valuations) are useful when there are lower levels of uncertainty. When uncertainty increases and forecasting becomes difficult, the value of quantitative approaches decreases. Engineers, executives, and managers need to address the critical nature of risk and uncertainty in the decision-making process.

Identification of the risks and uncertainties inherent in a proposed action, assessment of their impact on the possible outcomes, and design of contingency plans to manage them are essential for making sound project/business decisions. Without completing these activities, decisions made and undertaken are likely to be sub-optimal ones, leading to organizations being less competitive in the marketplace.

Knowledge of financial management helps in designing appropriate financial instruments and tools to optimize the performance of the project throughout the life cycle. Similarly, appropriate knowledge of uncertainties and risk, and training in modern techniques can help in managing and engineering the uncertainties and risks inherent in projects. Strategists focus on the qualitative aspects of projects relating to uncertainties or contingencies that can be identified and evaluated through a framework such as scenario planning. Some uncertainty is always present in economic decision-making, and thus, some type of sensitivity analysis must normally be done in an economic analysis (EA). In an EA, 'future costs' are 'predicted' and there is an element of uncertainty about these data. Even if actual cost data from past projects are used, it is assumed that these data are an accurate estimate of future costs. Thus, all data used in calculating life-cycle costs are actually based on assumptions. The sensitivity of an analysis is tested by evaluating a range of estimates for critical cost elements.

6.2. UNCERTAINTIES

In a generous sense, 'uncertainty' means 'lack of certainty', having variability. It is the potential deficiency in any phase or activity in the project formulation, or cost and benefit estimation process that is due to inherent variability or lack of knowledge.

Uncertainty can be defined as the lack of ability to predict outcome of parameters or foresee events that may impact the project. Uncertainties have a defined range of possible outcomes described by functions reflecting the probability for each outcome. Uncertainty functions can describe discrete events or continuous ranges of outcomes.

Once all costs and benefits have been estimated, the analysis can be performed and the alternatives ranked to show which is economically best. However, the analysis is not complete until it has been examined for areas of uncertainty. *Sensitivity analyses* are used to evaluate the effect of these uncertainties on the ranking of the alternatives.

6.3. SENSITIVITY ANALYSIS

6.3.1. Concept, Definition and Purpose

An engineering project may be composed of complex physical, economic and environmental systems. The system contains variables, and the financial outcome can be highly sensitive to changes in the variables.

In projects involving many input variables, sensitivity analysis is an essential ingredient of project building and quality assurance. Sensitivity analysis is a tool for characterizing the uncertainty associated with the project. It is the study of how variation (uncertainty) in the outcome of a project can be apportioned quantitatively, or qualitatively, to different sources of variation in the input of the project. It provides information about the potential impact of uncertainty in selected factors/parameters.

Sensitivity analysis can be used to determine/ascertain:

–   Factors that mostly contribute to the output variability
–   The region in the space of input factors for which the output variation is maximum
–   Interactions between variables
–   How a given output depends upon the input variables

6.3.2. Mode or Method of Sensitivity Analysis

Sensitivity analysis is performed by changing a particular variable or parameter while keeping all other variables or parameters constant, and observed how the output is changed. If a small change in a variable results in relatively large change (in percentage form) in its outcomes, the outcomes are said to be sensitive to that parameter. The variable or parameter which is most sensitive, very accurate data/estimation for that variable is necessary. Sensitivity analysis should be considered for evaluating both single project and alternative options.

Effects of discount rate, input cost, utility cost, labour cost, etc. can be checked. A rigorous sensitivity analysis can help establish which factors are most important in the life cycle analysis and accurate impacts on the decision-making.

6.3.3. General Guidelines

A general rule when considering cost data is to examine the input variables. Variables that significantly impact the total NPV or the benefits of an alternative are good candidates for sensitivity analysis.

An easy way to find the sensitivity of a variable is to examine the percentage change in NPV (or outcome) values versus the percentage change in the candidate variable. Use a more realistic range for varying a single factor. A rule of thumb is to examine all costs which are 20 percent or more of the total NPV for an alternative.

A sensitivity analysis can be developed by asking the question — which input variables should be tested? That is, are there dominant costs with uncertainties concerning their magnitudes or their times of occurrence? Assumptions and constraints must be examined to determine if their variation affects the input variables.

Throughout the entire economic analysis process, the analyst should use common sense in deciding which sensitivity analyses to perform. A 'sensitivity analysis' of the 'discount rate' used in the financial analysis is required. This analysis tests the effect of changes in discount rate on the ranking of alternatives.

If the ranking of alternatives shows that one is much less costly than the others, it is probably not necessary to evaluate small changes in costs that have no chance of reversing the ranking. It is when the magnitude or timing of a cost may affect the ranking or when the economic choice is not clear cut that further investigation is needed.

The simplest case is when there is uncertainty for one or more costs in one alternative. In this case, the analyst can rerun the analysis, inserting the upper (or lower) bound value for the cost(s) in question. This principle may also be applied for the timing of a cost.

The more complex situation is the general one in which one or more costs in each of the two alternatives has uncertainties associated with them. The solution to the complex situation is actually very simple. The NPV of each alternative is expressed as a function of the uncertain costs and then the NPVs are set equal to each other. The result is an equation in terms of the percentage change in the costs for each alternative.

6.4. RISK

6.4.1. Concept and Definition

The term 'risk' is considered and perceived as a negative outcome and contains elements of fear. *Risk* can be defined as the exposure to loss or gain (in any aspect of health, wealth, business), or the probability of occurrence of loss or gain multiplied by its respective magnitude. Events are said to be *certain* if the probability of their occurrence is 100%, or totally *uncertain* if the probability of occurrence is 0%. In between these extremes, the uncertainty varies quite widely.

The risks can be both 'endogenous' (i.e. internal to the project), and 'exogenous' (external, i.e. coming from the project environment). The internal risk may be due to: (1) duration and scope of projects, (2) the systemic effects, in case of large complex projects, (3) the irreversibility of many decisions, and (4) large number of stakeholders with diverse and often conflicting interests, etc.

Although a project may look potentially very favorable, but if the probability of the project succeeding is low or if the exposure is excessive, few decision makers/managers will be willing to authorize the project. The project manager/analyst/engineer should estimate the impact of the variability and uncertainties pertaining to risks, costs and scheduling. This assessment will enable it to estimate the project risk budget or the risk reserve and schedule contingency, which should be both considered (or factored in) when defining the total project cost of the infrastructure project. The fact is that, in the world of business, risk is inherent and unavoidable. Whilst one cannot completely control risk, one can certainly help to reduce uncertainty, and greatly increase the chances of project success.

6.4.2. Risk versus Uncertainties

Frequently, risk and uncertainty have been used interchangeably in the literature, but they have distinct theoretical constructs. *Risk* represents the probability distribution of the consequences of each alternative. A probability distribution implies an ability to quantify the consequences of an alternative. On the other hand, *uncertainty*, is applied when the consequences of each alternative belong to some subset of all possible consequences, but that the decision maker cannot assign definite probabilities to the occurrence of particular outcomes.

Uncertainty and risk are closely related (interrelated) and may do overlap (and also the agreement on the demarcation between risk and uncertainty is not universal). Quantifiable factors surrounding a capital project represent risks, whereas qualitative factors that affect decision-makers' confidence in project estimates represent uncertainties. As many investment decisions involve both quantitative and qualitative analyses, the results from differing methods of project evaluation must be optimized.

6.4.3. Types of Risks

Based on the type and characteristics of the project, the risk may be of different types: financial risk, construction risk, technical risk, market/competitive risks, regulatory/political risks, etc.

Financial risk: Changes in interest rate, inflation/deflation, credit limit (release/availability of budget for the project).

Construction risks: Time delay due to natural calamities or organizational difficulties, which can increase the cost of the project.

Technical risks: Failure of the structure due to external forces (e.g. earth quake), failure of machineries/instruments.

Market/Competitive risks: Loss of market because of better, earlier, or larger similar projects; loss of market due to substituting projects/industries.

Regulatory/Political risks: Changes in rules and regulations relevant to the project cycle (e.g. increase in tax for the input items, limit import of input item, etc.), changes in government and hence policy, which can limit to complete/open or receive funds for the target project.

Execution and/or operation risk: May be executed and/or operated properly or not.

A general format and sample list of assumptions and risks of a development project (generalized) is given in Table 6.1.

Table 6.1. Risks and assumptions (as may influence success/failure of the project) – Example

Particulars	Description
Assumptions	a) Weather condition during the project period will be normal b) Political environment will be normal c) Management will co-operate and the staffs will work efficiently d) Cost of the inputs will remain stable e) Necessary instruments will work properly f) Funds will be released in time
Risks	(a) Extreme weather events at the project period [e.g. in coastal zone, tropical storms and consequent tidal flood] may hamper the scheduled works and destroy some activities (b) Unstable political environment may delay the scheduled works

6.4.4. When to Conduct Risk Analysis

If there are multiple numerical uncertainties and these uncertainties cause concern, then the use of risk analysis techniques is advisable.

6.4.5. How to Conduct Risk Analysis

Risk analysis does not require extensive knowledge of statistics and probability theory. The following two key issues need to be understood:

- The probability of occurrence (probability number), which can influence decisions
- Measuring the variability of the quantity (upper and lower limit)

Methods of risk analysis include:

- Probabilistic analysis
- Sensitivity analysis
- Scenario analysis
- Monte Carlo Simulation

Steps in risk analysis (probabilistic analysis)
- Identify the critical variables
- Specify a range (for each variable)

- Determine probability within the range
- Risk = 1 – probability

Use of probability analysis (example):

- Use of probability technique for the determination of minimum height of levee/dam/retaining wall etc. which could save the target area/object/offshore installation from flooding.

6.4.6. Risk Management

Strategic measures to manage risks include:

– Protection against most serious risks
– High discount rate for risker project
– Design strategy

Design strategies include the use of technical, organizational, scheduling, and financial choices that reduce the chance and impact of risks (i.e. avoiding risky elements).

In projects, it is necessary to define one or a number of objective functions to represent the project under consideration and then measure the likelihood of achieving certain target values for them. Examples of such functions include capital expenditure, completion time, and so on. Risk management involves modeling the project's objective functions against project variables, which include such variables as cost and quantities of input resources, external factors, etc.

Since the project variables are often stochastic in nature and dynamic (i.e. exhibiting varying degrees of uncertainty over time) it is quite natural that the objective functions will also exhibit uncertainty. Project uncertainty is the probability that the objective function will not reach its planned target value.

If the project variables could be identified and characterized well in advance and provided that these were to remain basically unchanged during the period of the project then it would be possible to estimate the risks and/or variances of the objective functions. However, all of the project variables are not always identifiable, or their probability of occurrence may shift over time. Their impacts (both positive and negative) could also change as would their inter-relationships. These will then make the task of risk management extremely difficult.

6.4.7. Probability Analysis and Its Application in Risk Management

6.4.7.1. Concept of Probability

In our everyday life, we use the notion – 'probability'. Simply speaking, it is the chance of occurrence of an event. It is a mathematical basis for prediction. For an exhaustive set of outcomes, the probability of an event is the ratio of the outcomes that will produce a given event to the total number of possible outcomes. If we consider a coin having two sides – side-

1 (head) and side-2 (tail), and toss it unbiasly, the coin can lands either side-1 up or side-2 up. That is, the possibility or probability of either side-1 or side-2 is obviously 50 percent (possible outcome of side-1/ total number of possible outcome = $1/(1+1)$ = 0.50 or 50%).

The concept of probability can be applied in different aspects of hydrology. Regarding rainy days, it can be expected that there will always be some dry and wet days, and hence the dry-day or wet-day probability. Other forms of probability include flood probability, storm probability, frequency of occurrence of events (may be of particular magnitude of flood or storm or rainfall), etc. Probability is usually denoted with 'P', so that probability of an event x is simply P(x). It is expressed either as a decimal (≤ 1.0) or percentage by multiplying the decimal by 100.

6.4.7.2. Some Related Terminologies

Exceedance Probability

It denotes the probability that a given flood discharge (or a rainfall) event will be equaled or exceeded within a certain period of time.

Annual Exceedance Probability (AEP)

Annual exceedance probability is the probability of exceedance of a given event within a period of one year. Probability of non-exceedance = 1 - probability of exceedance

Risk

Risk is synonemous with exceedance probability. It is the probability of the occurrence of an undesirable event in a given number of observations.

Average Recurrence Interval (ARI)

Average recurrence interval is the average or expected value of the period between exceedance of a given event (e.g. rainfall, flood). The average frequency or recurrence interval does not imply periodicity. A 10 year frequency rain means that a rain which occurs on an average once in 10 years, e.g. 10 times in 100 years or 20 times in 200 years. It is not necessary that such a rain occurs only after 10 years; it may occur during 4 consecutive years and then not occur for 20 years.

Return Period

It is synonymous with recurrence interval. It is the average period in years within which an event (rainfall or flood) of specified magnitude will be equaled or exceeded.

6.4.7.3. Probability under Different Perspectives

Probability of occurrence of a rainfall or flood having a recurrence interval of T years, occurring in any year (the chance of its occurrence in any one year) i.e. the probability of exceedance, is:

P =

Probability of no T year rainfall occurring in any year (probability of non-exceedance) =
1- P =
Probability of no T year rainfall occurring in N years = ( )^N
Probability of at least one T year rainfall occurring in N years =
= 1 - ( )^N

6.4.7.4. Examples

Example #6.1.
Suppose we have an agricultural field protected from the adjacent river by a levee which
is designed to retain the one in 100 floods.
(a) What is the chance of the field being flooded in the next 25 years?
(b) If we wish to lower the risk to 1%, what ARI flood should the levee be designed for?

Solution:
Chance of the field being flooded in the next 25 years is
$P = 1 - ()^N$
$= 1 - ()^{25}$
$= 22\%$
i.e. approximately a ¼ th chance.
$(b)\ 0.01 = 1 - ()^{25}$
or, T = 2500 yrs

Example #6.2.
(a) What is the chance in any year of a wetland being flooded from an adjacent river
which has a natural levee that is overtopped on average once in every 5 years?

(a) In the next 5 years, what is the chance of the wetland not being flooded?

Solution
(a) Annual recurrence interval (ARI), T = 5 years
Annual expected probability, AEP = 1/T = 1/5 = 0.2 = 20 % chance of the wetland being
flooded in any year.

(b) P = 1 - ( )^5
= 67 % of the wetland being flooded in the next 5 yrs.

Therefore, there is a (1 − 0.67) = 33 % chance of the wetland not being flooded in the
next 5 yrs.

6.4.7.5. Decision Making under Risk and Uncertainty
Varying levels of risk and uncertainty can affect a decision-maker's choice of models,
techniques, and processes used for making the investment decision. Managers can employ
different analytical tools for different levels of uncertainty. In the case where uncertainty

increases, more qualitative approach (and tools) should be used, and should rely on judgment and experience to a greater extent. In the face of risk, the managers should use analytical, quantitative approaches to identify the optimal decision.

When considering risk and uncertainty jointly, the effect of uncertainty is dominant to that of risk. The implication here is that analytical, quantitative tools, even ones that can model dynamic decision-making, are not able to model the more qualitative nature of uncertainty. Instead of trying to quantify strategic management in the face of high uncertainty, we should be taking a more qualitative approach to the finance side of project analysis. The quantitative modelling frameworks often used for valuation purposes are useful, but their primary function may be to better qualitatively define, structure, and understand a project's uncertainties. To develop a corporate integrated risk management tool, the use of a qualitative, rather than a quantitative, real options approach, in conjunction with scenario planning, can be used.

6.5. UNCERTAINTIES, RISKS, AND THEIR MANAGEMENT IN WATER RESOURCES SECTOR

6.5.1. Perspectives

Evaluation of risks must be based not only on delivering projects on time and within budget but also on crafting, developing and operating a long term business entity which can deliver the business objectives of the parties concerned while meeting or exceeding community expectations.

Within the water resources sectors, reducing flood damages is a complex task that requires multidisciplinary understanding of the earth sciences and civil engineering. Dams, levees, and other river works must be sized to local conditions; geotechnical theories and applications help ensure that structures will safely withstand against potential hydraulic and seismic forces; and economic considerations must be balanced to ensure that reductions in flood damages are commensurate with project costs and associated impacts on social, economic, and environmental values.

Many flood damage reduction projects involve the construction of levees. The historical approach to coping with hydrologic and hydraulic uncertainties of large floods has been based on a best estimate of the levee height required to withstand a given flood, which is then augmented by a standard increment of levee height called "freeboard". The best estimate has traditionally been based on the expected height of a design flood (e.g., a 100-year flood, the magnitude of which has a 1 percent chance of being equaled or exceeded in any given year). Freeboard is then added above the expected height.

Multidisciplinary factors contribute to the risk of flooding in riverine systems. In hydrology, levees are evaluated for their ability to withstand the flood of a given magnitude, usually defined by a return period. In geotechnical engineering, levees are assessed for their stability and potential for failure by seepage through the embankment.

Among the various factors contributing to flood risk, only the flood-frequency component has traditionally been considered probabilistically. This component is indeed a major factor contributing to the flood risk, often accounting for more than 50 percent of the failure risk. But several other factors are significant and should be accounted for quantitatively.

6.5.2. Factors Affecting Risk in Flood Forecasting and Management

The following factors are often important in determining flood risks.

Hydrologic Factors

Hydrologic factors include flood frequency and volume and time distribution of the flood along the stream (which in turn depend on snow melt and/or rainfall characteristics), rainfall–runoff relationships of the watershed and the characteristics of the stream network.

Rainfall factors include spatial and temporal distributions of the precipitation, the sample representativeness, accuracy and adequacy of the rainfall data, and the methods of analysis or simulation. Similarly, there are uncertainties in the representativeness, accuracy, and adequacy of the flood data in both space and time, and in the methods used to analyze these uncertainties.

Watershed-stream factors include storage in lakes, reservoirs, and wetlands. There are also uncertainties in soil moisture, rain interception, and changing land uses.

Hydraulic Factors

Hydraulic factors include the nature of flood propagation in the channel and the equations and methods to simulate the flood propagation (which in turn depend on channel geometry), the roughness and slope of the channel bed, and the nature of the floodplain. Also included are the effects of hydraulic structures in the watershed, such as dams and spillways, levees, locks, weirs, sluices, gates, valves, bridges, intakes, and other diversion structures; also included are effects of sediment in the river, including erosion, scour, and deposition along the channel. Effects of wind and waves should also be considered.

Structural and geotechnical factors include geologic properties of the foundation, seepage through and cutoff beneath levees, internal erosion or piping of levee materials, strength instabilities in embankments or the subsurface, deep seepage failure away from the levee, and other soil mechanics issues.

Seismic factors (on dams and levees) include frequency and magnitude of earthquakes, fault and tectonic characteristics, earthquake-induced ground motion at the dam or levee site and liquefaction of foundation soil, and flooding probability associated with earthquake-induced dam or levee failure.

Materials and construction factors include type and quality of materials used for dams and levees, thermal and moisture variations affecting dam or levee quality during its service period and during its construction, and construction quality control.

Other geophysical factors include ice action in the river and on dams, levees or other structures, flash flooding from failure of dams, levees, or other facilities; thunder/lightning destruction; and tornado and other weather-related impacts.

Operational and maintenance factors include operational procedures on water diversion and release prior to and during flooding; operational procedures when an incident occurs;

safety inspections of the river system; regulations on boat traffic and fishing during flooding; repair and maintenance rules; grazing and other land uses; and vegetation cover and type.

6.5.3. Implications

While including uncertainty in economic analyses may impact performance indices. The influence of uncertainty on the expected value of performance criteria depends upon the nonlinearity of the models being used. A small uncertainty in the flow–stage relationship, or in the stage at which a levee fails, for example, can make a large difference in the reliability of a levee system and thus in project decisions. Risk analyses that explain the dynamics of a system and explain opportunities for interventions that improve system operation can be useful. At a minimum, risk analysis should identify which uncertainties are the most important.

To achieve the objective of using risk analyses to improve decision making, the remaining challenge is to compute other criteria that provide insight into system operation and into where cost-effective changes can be made to improve performance. Further scientific knowledge is needed to assess how risk analysis can best be used in making project decisions for flood hazard damage reduction.

6.5.4. General Guideline for Uncertainty Management

The management of risk and uncertainty should begin from appraisal phase. First, the objectives and demand are defined in feasibility study. After conceptual stage, the thorough description of construction decision's and solutions is preceded. It is advisable to take all possible design decisions in the beginning of evaluation phase before obtaining of construction permit, because later the effectiveness of change decrease and the price of changes increase.

To minimize project uncertainties and design ambiguities, it is advisable to consult with relevant experts, take professional opinion, employ the professional judgment, evaluate alternative solutions and finally reach a conclusion/decision at the very beginning of project implementation.

Risk analysis and management should not be viewed as a separate planning and response operation. Risk and opportunity management is a way of thinking and a philosophy that should permeate the entire spectrum of project activities.

6.6. ENVIRONMENTAL SCREENING

The environmental aspects of the proposed project(s) should be studied and prepared a summary table for decision making purpose. A proposed checklist for environmental aspects is given in Table 6.2.

Note:
- Depending on the objective and nature of the project, assessment would include only those specific issues which are relevant.
- Health, Safety and Environment (HSE) are the primary concerns and thus all to be centered around environment.
- Genetic Diversity: To cover Crop/Livestock/Fisheries/Forestry as applicable.
- Chemical Fertilizer: Single, imbalanced, use of contaminated one.
- Heavy Metal Contamination: From project activities by Arsenic, Lead, Cadmium or any other.
- Health Hazards: To be considered in respect of residual effect of pesticide, use of chemicals in preservation, processing and artificial ripening besides non-compliance to safety measures like, use of masks, gloves etc.
- Pollution: Quality aspects as influenced by the project activities.
- Small(less than 20%), Moderate (Between 20-50%) and Large (Over 50%)

[¥] If 'improvement' put '+' sign, and if 'deterioration' put '-' sign in front of the box chosen.

Table 6.2. Environmental Screening Matrix for development project (general format)

Sl. No.	Environmental issue	Component	Improvement/Deterioration[¥]				Remarks
			Small	Moderate	Large	None	
1	*Biodiversity*	Flora		+			
		Fauna		+			
		Genetic diversity		+			
		Exotic varieties		+			
		Local varieties/ cultivars		+			
		Hybrids				-	
2	*Soil quality*	Organic matter		+			
		Chemical fertilizer use		+			
		Soil salinity	-				
		Fertility status		+			
		Microbial activity		+			
		Heavy metal contamination				-	
		Water quality	-				
3	*Agro-Chemicals*	Pesticide use		+			
		POPs				-	
		IPM				-	
		Pest infestation	-				
		Bio-pesticides				-	
		Health hazard				-	
4	*Pollution*	Soil				-	
		Water				-	
		Air				-	

6.7. FINAL SELECTION OF PROJECT

Taking into account the financial ranking, risk status, and environmental aspects; final selection of the project *or* the decision should be made applying the professional judgment.

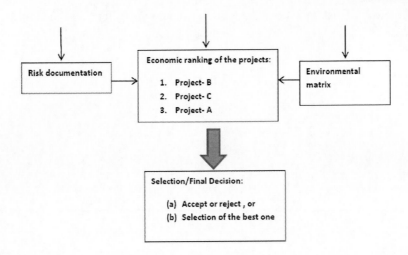

Exercise

6.1. Mention the assumptions, risks, and uncertainties in the following branches of civil engineering projects; and also suggest possible measures to reduce the risk and uncertainties:

(a) Structural
(b) Geotechnical
(c) Mining
(d) Roads and highway
(e) Renewable energy
(f) Water resources

6.2. Perform sensitivity analysis of the following project cash-flow for:

(a) Discount rate (r)
(b) Input cost
(c) Production rate
(d) Price of the product

Discount rate = 10%

Year	0	1	2	3
Cost ($)	20000	7000	1000	1000
Product unit (nos)	0	2000	2000	3000
Unit price of product, $		10	10	10

6.3. A town is to be protected from the river-flood. It is suggested to design a retaining wall to retain one in 150 flood.

    (a) What is the chance of the town being flooded in the next 25 years of wall construction?

    (b) To lower the risk to 2%, what ARI flood should the wall be designed for?

Chapter 7

TIME FOR EQUIPMENT REPLACEMENT

The Equipment replacement system is one of the industrial problems for management. A large amount of annual capital investment needs correct information for proper allocation and utilization. The replacement timing, selection, and method used for reaching decisions are some of the important factors in the efficient operation and utilization of the resource. Replacement decisions are more important in market oriented economy where competition of the market is bringing profit margins to be minimal.

7.1. BACKGROUND

The performance of almost everything declines with age - such as machines, cars, bikes, etc. Although a routine maintenance can keep the equipment working efficiently for a certain period, as time goes by, equipment deteriorates (Frequent breakdowns occur, defective output increases, unit labor costs rise, and production schedules cannot be met) and becomes obsolete. There comes a point when the efficiency becomes too low, repairs are too expensive and it is less expensive to buy a replacement. We must decide whether we should keep an existing unit of equipment or replace it with a new unit.

One of the most commonly performed engineering economy studies is that of replacement or retention of an asset or system that is currently installed. This differs from "Cost analyses" studies where all the alternatives are new. The fundamental question answered by a replacement study about an installed (recent past) asset or system is: "Should it be replaced now or later?" If the decision is to replace, the study is complete. If the decision is to retain, the cost estimates and decision will be revisited each year.

7.2. THE NEED FOR A REPLACEMENT STUDY

Replacement may be needed or becomes inevitable due to the following reasons:

1. For improving *or* maintaining production capacity
2. For diversification *or* change of product
3. To improve the quality of product

4. To avoid excessive maintenance cost
5. To decrease labor number, and hence production cost
6. To increase efficiency of the production (i.e. to decrease the input required, such as fuel, raw materials)
7. Intermittent demand (technological or others)

Reduced Performance

Physical deterioration, reduced reliability or productivity - this usually results in increased costs of operation, higher scrap and rework costs, lost sales, reduced quality, diminished safety, and larger maintenance expenses.

Altered Requirements – Intermittent Demand

New requirements of accuracy, speed, or other specifications cannot be met by the existing equipment or system (complete replacement, retrofitting or augmentation).

Obsolescence

International competition and rapidly changing technology make currently used systems and assets perform acceptably but less productively than equipment coming available. The decreased development cycle time to bring new products to market is often the reason for premature replacement studies, that is, studies performed before the estimated useful or economic life is reached. Replacement may also be initiated due to lack of spares. Even though a machine is working perfectly to the satisfaction of the organization due to shift of production type, bankruptcy, or else the supplier may stop production of such spare parts. For lucky areas batch-producing companies may take the responsibility to supply spares. But overall, the cost of spares will be extremely high where it is not bearable to continue.

During operation, machines may fail due to technical problems or mal-operation. In such cases, replacement is initiated not on the formal way of replacement system. In formal way, machines are replaced after completing their life. The changes may be planned and programmed due to being beyond maintainability. From the commencement of production, industries strive at least to meet the design capacity of their industry if not improvement.

To meet this requirement the bottle neck machines are replaced or additional machines are installed. Technical and process audit of the factory and machinery are carried out for identifying deficiencies which hinder achieving of the designed capacity and optimum efficiency. Further increase of production capacity or change of the production system, are some of the reasons for replacement of equipment.

To meet the demand level, most industries either slowly or at a fast rate make changes in production rate or production system, and type of product. To do these changes, it is inevitable to change the layout of the machinery, tools etc. These changes bring about a complete replacement of small or large machineries. With this type of revolution, the machines to be replaced may not be at the state of replacement stage either technologically or physically. Whether a machine is in a good state or not, if there is expansion in any aspect the equipment may be removed, or will be allowed to work in parallel, put as a standby or transplanted. During this time the amount of capital on these machines is considered in the following way:

- Some of the equipments may have good salvage values so that the market may absorb them and others may be discarded as a scrap.
- Some of the machines may be rebuilt/rehabilitated and start a new life with the system,
- Some of the machines may not be touched at all. Only additional machines in parallel may be installed.

7.3. FACTORS AFFECTING REPLACEMENT

7.3.1. Basic Factors

Generally, the following factors affect the replacement decision:

(a) **For the existing one (also termed as "Defender")**

- Equipment type
- Present capacity
- Year of purchase
- Purchase price
- Service years
- Down time records due to machine failure
- Any wastage of product due to machine failure
- Annual maintenance cost (at least for 3- 4 years)
- Book value of the machine at present
- Salvage value, if it is sold now and also in future.

(b) **For the proposed new one (also termed as "Challenger")**

- Price
- Source of fund
- Capacity
- Efficiency Rating
- Estimated life expectancy
- Warranty Coverage
- Expenses required for installation
- Influences on other machines due to the changes
- Other re-arrangements required (if any)
- Any additional expenses expected

7.3.2. Other Considerations

The parts replacement decision - to replace a piece of equipment, should be based on condition and value of the parts. The same applies for the whole equipment. The judgment should be the result of weighing the costs of keeping the old equipment against the cost of its replacement. The new equipment costs money, and the question that comes to us is: "Will the advantages of the new equipment be great enough to justify the investment it requires?"

We can answer this question by making a cost comparison. To recognize the better alternative we need to know the total cost of each alternative - keeping the old equipment or buying a replacement. Once these costs are determined, you can compare them and identify the more economical equipment. For that, we must consider several cost elements and revenue when computing the total cost of the old and new equipment:

- Depreciation
- Interest
- Operating Costs
- Revenues

Depreciation

One of the costs connected with any type of equipment is 'depreciation'. When considering equipment replacement, we must calculate the future depreciation expense that we will experience with both the old and the new equipment.

We have to determine the depreciation expense for the old equipment in the same general way but for one import difference. The difference is that no expenditure is required to procure the equipment because you already own it. However, a decision to keep it does require an investment at the present time. This investment is equal to the asset's market value - that is, to the amount of money the asset would bring in if it were replaced and sold. If this amount is not equal to the equipment's book value, the depreciation expense that was shown for accounting purposes is in error because it did not reflect the actual depreciation.

So, to determine the actual future depreciation expense that will be experienced with the old equipment, you must know:

(1) its present market value,
(2) its estimated remaining service life, and
(3) its expected salvage value at the end of that life.

The difference between the present market value and the future salvage value represents the amount by which the equipment will depreciate during its remaining life in your business/production.

Interest

In addition to depreciation, every piece of equipment generates an interest expense. This expense occurs because owning an asset ties up some of your capital. If you had to borrow this capital you would have to pay for the use of the money. This "out-of-pocket" cost is one of the costs of owning the equipment.

When you use your own money, in this case, the amount involved is no longer available for other investments which could bring you a return. This "opportunity cost" is one of the costs of owning the equipment. Suppose that the market value of an asset during a given year is $10,000. Suppose also that at the same time, you are getting capital at a cost of 15 percent per year. On the other hand, suppose that if you converted the asset into cash, you could invest the money and realize a rate of return of 15 percent per year. In either case, a decision to own that asset during that year would be costing you 15 percent of $10,000, or $1,500 in interest.

Thus, in any comparison of equipment alternatives, you must take the cost of money into account. So, when determining whether or not existing equipment should be replaced, you must estimate what money is costing you in terms of a percent per year.

Operating Costs

There is a third type of cost - *the cost of operation*, that is experienced with a piece of equipment. Typical operating costs are expenditures for labor, materials, supervision, maintenance, and power.

These costs must be considered because your choice of equipment affects them. You may find it convenient to estimate these costs on an annual basis. You can get figures for each unit of equipment by estimating its next-year operating costs as well as the annual rate at which these costs are likely to increase as wage rates rise and the equipment deteriorates.

For example, operating cost for a new equipment is likely to be $10,000 during the first year of its life. You might also estimate that after the first year, the operating costs will increase at a rate of $500 a year. You can simplify the problem of estimating these costs by either (1) ignoring those costs that are the same for the old and the new equipment, or (2) estimating only the differences between the operating costs of the two units. With this simplification, the total costs which you calculate for each type of equipment will be understated by the same amount. Therefore, the difference between these total costs will remain the same, and you will still be able to recognize the more economical alternative.

Revenues

Often, the revenues generated by the old and the new equipment will be the same. When this is true, revenues can be ignored for the same reason that you can ignore equal operating costs. But if revenues are affected by the choice of equipment, they must be considered. For example, we can estimate that the higher quality of output from the new equipment will increase annual sales by $2,000. You can handle this difference in revenues in either of two ways. One way is to show the $2,000 as an additional annual cost that will be experienced with the old equipment. The other way is to treat the $2,000 as a negative annual cost and associate it with the new equipment. The total cost which you calculate will be affected by your choice of method, but the difference between these costs will remain the same.

Expressing the Cost in an Annual Average

In brief, you can make the necessary cost analysis on the new and old equipment only after you have the proper data for each. For the new equipment, the data include first cost, service life, salvage value, operating costs, and revenue advantage. For the old equipment, the data include market value, remaining service life, future salvage value, and operating costs. In addition, for both alternatives, the cost of money must be stated in the form of interest amount.

By using these data, you can determine the elements of the total costs. These elements consist of depreciation expense, interest expense, operating costs, and possibly lost revenues. Now, it so happens that these costs can be expressed in a variety of ways.

However, the simplest way for cost comparison purposes is to describe these cost elements in terms of an average annual cost. Doing so permits you to calculate and compare the total average annual costs of the old and new equipment and reach a decision.

A general replacement policy on deteriorating equipment indicates the best period of replacement from the financial point of view to be when the equivalent uniform annual cost starts to increase. But for heavy capital-intensive equipment with little resale value, such as a generator, it should be used as long as possible, until the maintenance cost becomes excessively high. A capital item with a significant resale value, such as a car, should be replaced keeping the resale value in mind.

7.3.3. Explanation Example

The Old Equipment

Let us consider some facts about an old piece of equipment. Assume that it has a market value of $7,000. If retained, its service life is expected to be four (4) years, and its salvage value is expected to be $1,000. Say, the cost of money (interest) is 12 percent per year. Assume that, operating cost for the next year is estimated to be $8,000 and will increase at an annual rate of $200. With this set of information, we can obtain the total average annual cost of the alternative of keeping this equipment.

Annual Depreciation Expense

Let we begin by calculating the equipment's average annual depreciation expense. You can do this by determining the total depreciation and dividing that amount by the asset's four-year life. Your answer is $ 1,500 which you get as follows:

Annual depreciation = ($7,000 - $1,000)/4
= $ 1500

Annual Interest Expense

Next, you can calculate the average annual interest expense. The maximum investment in the equipment is $7,000, its present market value. But as time goes by, the investment in the asset decreases because its market value decreases. The minimum investment is reached at the end of the equipment's life when it has a salvage value of $1,000. The average investment will be the average of these maximum and minimum values. You calculate it as follows:

Average investment = ($7,000 + $1,000)/2
= $ 4,000

To determine the average annual interest expense, you multiply the average investment ($4,000, in this example) by the annual interest rate of 12 percent. Doing so yields:

Annual Interest = $4,000 × (12/100) = $ 480

Annual Operating Costs
You can determine the average annual operating costs by computing the average of the individual annual operating costs. In this example, assume that they are estimated to be $8,000, $8,200, $8,400, and $8,600.

Annual operating costs = ($8,000 + $8,200 + $8,400 + $8,600)/4
= $8,300

Total Average Annual Cost
For the old equipment, the total average annual cost is simply the sum of the calculated average annual cost for: (1) depreciation, (2) interest, and (3) operating expenses. This sum is $10,280, as shown below.

Item Average annual cost

Depreciation	$ 1,500
Interest	$ 480
Operating Costs	$ 8,300
Total	$10,280

The New Equipment
Let us consider now the facts on a piece of new equipment which may be a replacement for the old equipment. Assume that the first cost of this new equipment is $30,000. Its life is estimated to be ten years, and it will probably have a salvage value of $6,000. Operating costs with this equipment are expected to average $5,200 a year. Furthermore, it is estimated to have an annual revenue advantage of $300 over the old equipment. The cost of money is 12 percent per year.

Follow the same approach as you did for the old equipment to determine the total average annual cost of this new equipment.

Annual Depreciation Expense
You can start with the average annual depreciation expense.
Annual depreciation = ($30,000 - $6,000)/10
= $2,400

Annual Interest Expense
To obtain the average annual interest expense, multiply the average investment in this asset by the interest rate. The average investment is $18,000 (one-half of the sum of the $30,000 first cost and the $6,000 salvage value). The average annual interest expense is $2,160 obtained as follows:

Annual interest = [($30,000 + $6,000)/2] × (12/100) = $2,160

Total Average Annual Cost

When you also take the estimated operating costs and revenue advantage into account, you find the total average annual cost to be $9,460, as shown below (Item Average annual cost):

Depreciation + Interest + Operating cost - Revenue advantage = (2400 + 2160 + 5200) - 300 = $9,760 - $ 300 = $ 9460

The Comparison

When we have the total average annual cost for the old and the new equipment, we are ready to compare the two. In the example, the calculated annual cost is $10,280 for the old equipment and $9,460 for the new. On the surface, the new equipment is more economical than the old.

You may argue that with the old equipment you are committing yourself for only four years, whereas with the new, your commitment is for ten years. This fact suggests a need for considering the kind of equipment that may be available for replacement purposes four years from now as compared with ten years from now. But no one can forecast that far into the future. It is best to ignore the nature of future replacements in your computations and assume that the replacement available four years from now will have the same annual cost as the one available ten years from now.

Irreducible Factors

When your calculated annual costs show that the one unit of equipment has a decided advantage over the other, you can usually select the better alternative by comparing these calculated costs. But what do you do when the annual costs of the old and the new equipment do not differ greatly? In such a case, you should consider the fact that the estimates might contain errors and that there are things on which a dollar value cannot be placed. So you may have to base your decision on *irreducible factors* - factors that cannot be reduced to dollars and cents.

A few examples will suggest the nature of such factors:

- First, if total average annual costs are about the same, you will probably favor the equipment that required the smaller investment and has the shorter life. The same will hold true when you suspect that technological advances will result in more efficient equipment becoming available in the near future.
- As another example, you will prefer the equipment which has greater output capacity, safety, and reliability even though the value of these is unknown.
- And finally, when you suspect that interest rates and the price of new equipment will increase significantly, you will be inclined to invest in new equipment now rather than later.

7.3.4. Other Considerations in Replacement Study

There are several additional aspects of a replacement study that may be introduced:

- Future-year replacement decisions at the time of the initial replacement study.
- Opportunity-cost versus cash-flow approaches to alternative comparison.
- Anticipation of improved future challengers.

In most cases when management initiates a replacement study, the question is best framed as, "Replace now, 1 year from now, 2 years from now, etc.?" The procedure answers this question provided the estimates for Challenger (C) and Defender (D) do not change with time. If estimates change over time, the decision to retain the defender may be prematurely reversed in favor of a better challenger.

The first costs (P values) for the *challenger* and *defender* are to be correctly taken as the initial investment for the challenger C and current market value for the defender D. This is called the opportunity-cost approach because it recognizes that a cash inflow of funds equal to the market value is forgone if the defender is selected.

7.4. REPLACEMENT METHOD/PROCEDURE

7.4.1. Earlier Replacement Models

Terborgh's Model

Terborgh (1949) was the first to develop a theory for equipment replacement based on explicitly stated assumptions of a linear operating cost function that is time-dependent with known constant parameter values. He presented procedures for comparing current equipments with challengers and descendants.

$$E = \frac{(n-1)}{2}c + \left[\frac{A-S}{n} + \frac{r}{2}(A+S)\right] \tag{7.1}$$

where
  C = the inferiority gradient, or the constant rate of cost accumulation due to operating inferiority
  A = the acquisition cost
  S = the salvage value
  r = the rate of return on capital investments within the firm
  n = the age of the equipment

The combined cost per year E is a sum of two terms; the first increases with equipment age (operating inferiority) and the second decreases with increasing age (capital cost).

The first term in the brackets of above eqn. is the average capital cost per year.

The second term in the bracket is approximately the average yearly cost of money over the period calculated by taking the cost of (A-S) for a period of n-i years, in which payments are made annually, plus the cost of borrowing S amount of money for n years.

Orenstein's Model

A development by Orenstein (1956) in the event of equal depreciation payments is that the economic life is independent of rate of return for an annual cost-minimization model. Orenstein considers three costs: (i) Acquisition cost, (ii) Annual rate of return on capital, r (iii) Linear operating cost, $F+dt$.

He defined the economic life as one that minimizes the average annual sum of the above,

$$E = \frac{A}{t} + r\frac{A}{2} + \left[F_t + \frac{t(t+1)}{2}d\right]\frac{1}{t}$$

$$\frac{d_E}{d_t} = -\frac{A}{t^2} + \frac{d}{2} = 0$$

$$t_0 = \sqrt{\frac{2A}{d}}$$

(7.2)

The economic life is then the value of t_0 such that

$$\frac{dt_0}{2} = \frac{A_0}{t_1}$$

where, d = increase in operating cost or the average increase in operating cost, is equal to the annual depreciation value of the equipment. The selection of alternative equipments would depend on the minimum values of the total average costs over the life of each. Obsolescence is considered to be introduced by increasing the interest rate, decreasing the life expectancy, or decreasing the salvage value.

Sandiford, Bernholtz, and Shelson Model

The models considered so far have assumed analytic forms for the cost functions. Sandiford, Bernholtz, and Shelson (1956) considered arbitrary values for the annual costs and developed numerical, iterative procedures for determining the economic life of vehicles.

The measure of performance chosen was the average annual cost over the replacement interval. The optimal policy was use of that replacement interval which minimized the average annual cost, to be determined for each group of vehicles. The total average cost C was considered to be the sum of capital wastage (acquisition cost less salvage value), interest, repair costs, and un-serviceability costs.

Values of C were calculated from historical data for each vehicle class by taking the cumulative averages and the minimum obtained by inspection. The authors used historical data to obtain optimum replacement intervals.

The Analogue of Fetter and Goodman

Fetter and Goodman (1957) have developed an electronic analogue of the equipment replacement model and have used it to solve the cost-minimization model formulated by Terborgh as one application. In addition, a number of models are developed where the solution is that replacement interval that maximizes the present value of all future returns from the firm's use of equipment.

Latest Developments

The importance and cruciality of equipment replacement decisions is one of the major challenges to organizations where the outcome is directly reflected on the organizations change on production costs/rate, changes on the financial statement or change on capacity of proper utilization of throughput, etc. Latest development on equipment replacement decisions is fully supported with the available tools, computers, to handle and process data to get meaningful information.

Nowadays the study on equipment replacement is focusing on implementation method and systems. Due to this, the studies made are more specialized to specific firms.

7.4.2. Economic Service Life (ESL) Method

A replacement study is an application of the annual worth (AW) method of comparing unequal life alternatives. In a replacement study with no specified time period, the AW values are determined by a technique of cost evaluation called the economic service life (ESL) analysis.

The economic service life (ESL) is the number of years n that the equivalent uniform annual worth of costs is the minimum, considering the most current cost estimates over all possible years that the asset may provide a needed service.

The ESL is determined by calculating the total AW of costs if the asset is in service 1 year, 2 years, 3 years, and so on, up to the last year the asset is considered useful. Total AW of costs is the sum of capital recovery (CR), which is the AW of the initial investment and any salvage value, and the AW of the estimated annual operating cost (AOC), that is:

Total AW of Cost = - Capital recovery – AW of annual operating costs
$$= - CR - AW \text{ of AOC}$$

The ESL is the n value for the smallest total AW of costs. Figure 7.1 shows the characteristic shape of a total AW of cost curve. The CR component of total AW decreases, while the AOC component increases, forming the concave shape. The two AW components are calculated as follows.

– The capital recovery is the AW of investment; it decreases with each year of ownership.
– Capital recovery is calculated using Equation [7.3], the salvage value S that usually decreases with time is the estimated market value (MV) in that year.

Capital recovery = P - S   (7.3)

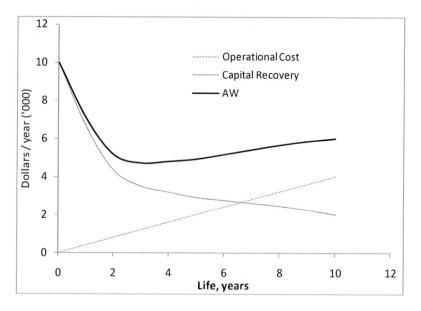

Figure 7.1. Schematic shape of a total AW of cost curve.

7.4.3. Reasons for Delaying Equipment Replacement

Some of the possible reasons for delaying the replacement of equipment beyond the economic replacement time are:

– Management tends to be conservative in decisions regarding the replacement of costly equipment.
– There may be a limitation on funds available for purchasing new equipment, but no limitation on funds for maintaining existing equipment.
– The present equipment is operational and is producing an acceptable quality product.
– The firm is making a profit with its present equipment.
– There is risk or uncertainty associated with predicting the expenses of a new machine, whereas one is relatively certain about the expenses of the current machine.
– There may be considerable uncertainty concerning the future demand for the services of the equipment in question.
– An anticipation that technological improvements in the future might render obsolete the equipment available currently; a wait-and-see attitude prevails.

7.4.4. Possible Errors in Replacement Studies

Several possible errors may occur in replacement studies. These may be due to:

– failure to recognize the true nature of depreciation accounting as a time allotment against future dates of money already spent

- failure to understand clearly the nature of cost accounting allocations
- unrealistic use of unit costs

Frequently made errors include:

1. Considering the excess of present book value over the net realizable value of the old asset as an addition to the investment in the new asset. This error increases the apparent cost associated with the new asset, and thus tends to prevent replacements that are really economical.
2. Calculating depreciation and interest (i.e., capital recovery) on the old asset on the basis of its original cost rather than its present net realizable value. This usually increases the apparent costs associated with the old asset, and thus tends to favor replacements that are really uneconomical.
3. Where indirect costs (burden) are allotted in the cost accounting system in proportion to direct costs (usually in proportion to direct labor cost), assuming without investigation that a reduction of direct expenditures will effect a corresponding saving in indirect expenditures. This error usually makes the apparent saving from proposed replacements greater than the saving that is actually possible to realize, and thus tends to favor replacements that are really uneconomical.
4. In cases where the proposed new asset provides more capacity than the old asset, comparing calculated unit costs realizable only with full-capacity operation, rather than comparing the actual costs realizable with the expected output. Where such excess of capacity is not likely to be used, this unit cost comparison tends to favor the asset with the surplus capacity, and is therefore favorable to replacements that are really uneconomical.

7.5. WORKOUT PROBLEM

Example 7.1.

A 5-years old industrial machine is being considered for early replacement. Its current market value is $15000. Estimated market value and annual operating costs for the next five (05) years are given below. Find out the optimum time for replacement of the machine. Assume interest rate of 8% per year.

Year	Estimated market value ($)	Annual operating cost ($)
1	12000	2600
2	8000	2800
3	6000	3100
4	2000	3400
5	0	4400

Solution

We know,

Total annual worth of cost =

(Capital recovery + Annual worth of operating cost)   (i)

Capital recovery (CR) for a particular year =

Market value in the preceding year (before initiation of the year) –

Salvage value at the end of the year   (ii)

Present value/worth (PW) of CR for a particular year N, $= F/(1+r)^N$

Similarly, the Present worth (PW) of annual operating costs (AOC) are calculated.

The results are summarized below.

Sample illustration for year 1:

Capital recovery, CR = 15000 - 12000 = 3000

PW of CR $= 3000/(1+0.08)^1 = 277.8$

PW of AOC $= 2600/(1+0.08)^1 = 2407.4$

Total AW of cost = (PW of CR + PW of AOC) = (2777.8 + 2407.4) =

= 5185.2

Year	Market value ($)	CR ($)	PW of CR ($)	AOC ($)	PW of AOC ($)	Total AW of cost ($)
0	15000					
1	12000	3000	2777.8	2600	2407.4	5185.2
2	8000	4000	3429.4	2800	2400.5	5829.9
3	6000	2000	1587.7	3100	2460.9	**4048.5**
4	2000	4000	2940.1	3400	2499.1	5439.2
5	0	2000	1361.2	4400	2994.6	4355.7

From the results, it is revealed that at year 3, the total annual value of cost is minimum. Hence, the machine should be replaced at year 3. (**Ans.**)

Exercise

(1) Why replacement of equipment or its parts is needed?

(2) What are the factors affecting equipment replacement? Discuss other relevant considerations in equipment replacement.

(3) Write short note on the following replacement models:

(a) Terborgh's Model

(b) Orenstein's Model

(c) Sandiford, Bernholtz, and Shelson Model

(d) The Analogue of Fetter and Goodman

(4) Discuss the Economic Service Life (ESL) method for equipment replacement.

(5) "For some reasons the equipment replacement is delayed" – Discuss

(6) What are the possible errors in replacement studies?

(7) A 7-years old manufacturing machine is being considered for early replacement. Its current market value is $12000. Estimated market value and annual operating costs for the next six (06) years are given below. If the interest rate is 10% per year, find out the optimum year for replacement of the machine.

Year	Estimated market value ($)	Annual operating cost ($)
1	12000	3600
2	10000	4200
3	8500	4400
4	7000	4600
5	4000	5000
6	0	5500

(8) The following Table shows the resale value and running cost of a machine corresponding to forthcoming years. If the present value of the machine is $20000 and interest rate is 5%, suggest the best time to replace the machine.

Next years	Resale value ($)	Running cost ($)
1	18000	4600
2	16000	4700
3	13000	4800
4	10000	5000
5	5000	5200
6	2000	5500
7	0	5700

REFERENCES

Fetter, R. B., and Googman, T. P. (1957). An Equipment Investment analog. *Opns. Res.*, 5: 657-669.

Grant, E. (1975). *Principles of Engineering Economy*, New Delhi: Prentice Hall of India, Inc, 5th ed.

Orenstein, R , B., (1956)." Topic on the MAPI Formula," *J. Ind. Eng.*, 7, 283-298.

Sandiford, P. J., Bernholth, B., and Shelton, W. (1956). Three applications of Operations Research in a Large Electric. *Opns. Res.*, 4: 663-673.

Terborgh, George (1949). *Dynamic Equipment policy*. McGraw-Hill Book Co., New York.

Chapter 8

MODELS AND SOFTWARES IN ECONOMIC AND FINANCIAL ANALYSIS

8.1. BASICS OF MODEL: GENERAL CONCEPTS

A model is a useful tool in obtaining answers in the choice of a decision or policy. By definition, model is a simplified representation of reality. It serves as a means of predicting and examining an existing or proposed system's performance under a set of conditions specified by the users. A model can come in many shapes, sizes, and styles. It may be a system of equations that show how parameters and variables of interest are related to one another. It is important to note that a model is not the real world but only an approximation of reality. In general all models have an information input, an information processor, and an output of expected results (Figure 8.1).

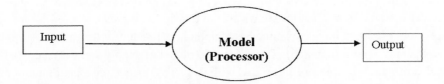

Figure 8.1. Schematic representation of a model.

8.2. ECONOMIC MODEL

8.2.1. Concept, Functions, Types, and Formulation

Almost all managerial decisions are based on forecasts. Every decision becomes operational at some point in the future, so it should be based on forecasts of future conditions. Forecasts are needed continually, and as time moves on, the impact of the forecasts on actual performance is measured; original forecasts are updated; and decisions are modified, and so on. The decision-maker uses forecasting models to assist him or her in decision-making process. The decision-making often uses the *modeling process* to investigate the impact of different courses of action retrospectively; that is, "as if" the decision has already been made under a course of action. The purpose of models is to aid in designing solutions. They are to assist understanding the problem and to aid deliberation and choice by allowing us to evaluate the consequence of our action before implementing them.

Economic models are simplified descriptions of reality (real life economies) used by economists. Modeling provides a logical, abstract template to help organize the analyst's thoughts.

The model helps the economist logically isolate and sort out complicated chains of cause and effect and influence between the numerous interacting elements in an economy. Through the use of a model, the economist can experiment, at least logically, producing different scenarios, attempting to evaluate the effect of alternative policy options.

An economic model includes several economic variables and describes the nature of the logical relationships between these variables.

A variable is just the value of an economic quantity, such as the rate of interest or the price of a good. The assumptions often involve holding some variables constant and only allowing one or two variables of interest to change. The relationships between the variables can be expressed graphically, mathematically or verbally.

Economic models fulfill two functions. The first is to describe some aspect of the reality of an economic phenomenon. The second is to assist economists in understanding the economy. In order to fulfill both of these functions, economic models are simplified versions of reality, with many real life variables removed. This makes models easier to understand, but it may also be less descriptive of the economic reality.

There are two basic types of economic models: qualitative and quantitative. Qualitative models are usually expressed in words, while quantitative models are expressed in mathematics or a graphical format. Other categories of economic models include accounting, aggregate and optimizing models.

Economic data is used to construct mathematical models. These models illustrate the way in which the allocation of scarce resources, such as goods and services, actually happens. For instance, the basic economic model known as the demand curve can be used to predict how the cost (value) of something can change based upon how much of it is available (supply) and how many people want it (demand). Thus, a simple model of supply and demand can be used to predict how much people are generally willing to pay to get their hands on something scarce.

Endogenous and Exogenous Variable

In context to economic model, variables may be *endogenous* or *exogenous*. A variable is said to be *endogenous* if it is determined within the model. Its value becomes known when the model is solved. For example, if the final level of demand is determined by the model's solution, demand is an endogenous variable.

On the other hand, if the value of a variable comes from outside the model, it is called *exogenous* variable. In macroeconomics, many policy variables such as the income tax rate *or* money supply growth rate, are treated as exogenous (as they are determined by the policy makers, rather than within the model).

8.2.2. Objectives of Economic and Financial Model Study

(a) The most important objective of financial analysis of any project is to *assess the financial impact* of projects on the farmers and enterprises involved, as well as any others who may be affected by the project.

This is achieved by analyzing all costs and benefits due to the project and by forecasting them into the foreseeable future, in order to project the net financial effect on all actors involved.

(b) A second equally important objective of financial analysis is the *preparation of financial plans or scenarios.*

These financial or business plans are somehow indirectly obtained while in the process of assessing the impact of the project or, to put it another way, they are the means through which project financial assessment is usually made. Financial analysis is also concerned with the measurement of performance against set targets on every aspect of the project. It identifies the *efficiency of use of resources* and provides the tools of improving overall performance. It also measures the effectiveness of management in mobilizing the factors of production for the achievement of financial goals and supports the search for improved approaches.

8.2.3. Purpose of Economic Model

Purposes of economic model include:

1. To analyze the financial consequences of current (e.g. farming) practices and proposed management actions.
2. Formulate the without-project scenario in the financial and economic analysis, taking into account underlying trends in technology, policy, local economy and physical environment in the project and wider system area, in order to reflect changes in productivity (positive or negative) that would have occurred without the intervention.

8.2.4. Scenario Analysis with Economic Model

Three broad types of analysis, coupled with modeling tools, are conducted within the economic policy analysis activities:

- *Market analysis*—analyzing existing and emerging markets, cost, and performance trends
- *Value analysis*—developing methods and tools for improving the quantification of the benefits and costs of distributed present value (PV).
- *Policy analysis*—analyzing reliability, security, and time-of-use value of PV, and the potential policy initiatives and proposals at the federal and state levels.

8.2.5. Some Relevant Definitions

System

Systems are formed with parts put together in a particular manner in order to pursue an objective. The relationship between the parts determines what the system does and how it functions as a whole. Therefore, the relationships in a system are often more important than the individual parts. In general, systems those are 'building blocks' for other systems, are called *subsystems*.

Validation and Verification

As part of the calibration process of a model, the modeler must validate and verified the model. The term validation is applied to those processes, which seek to determine whether or not a model is correct with respect to the "real" system.

Verification, on the other hand, seeks to answer the question "Are we building the system right?"

Delphi Analysis

Delphi Analysis is used in the decision making process, in particular in forecasting. Several "experts" sit together and try to compromise on something upon which they cannot agree.

8.2.6. Fields of Application of Economic Model

Economic models can be applied in the following areas (relevant to engineers):

–   Natural resources use and management
–   Renewable energy resource (all types)
–   Biomass production for energy (energy crop)
–   Engineering structures (all types)
–   Industries (all types)
–   Business options
–   Petroleum/Mining
–   Engineering technologies/Instruments/Processes selection
–   Agricultural production
–   Economic/ Other policy analysis
–   Market analysis
–   Program analysis

8.2.7. Notes on Different Models in Economics

Economists use the scientific approach for developing economic theories. Considering the way to test a theory, in economics it is not easy as it is in the scientific world; scientists can make an experiment under the controlled environment or the given conditions to test their theories. How do economists make a real experiment in economic system which is concerned with the real society? In this case they need specific tools, i.e. model/software.

Models provide a very useful decision making tool to the investor (state/public or private). BIOSEM, RECAP, BEAM, BIOCOST, BEAVER, MULTISEES, ECONPACK are some economic models/softwares, developed by research institutes in Europe and the USA, that carry out cost, technical, environmental and social analysis of bio-energy chains. Anyone can have query in mind regarding exactly what questions the models are capable to answer and which model or models should be used in various situations. No single model can answer all the questions. Therefore, synopsis of various models is offered below, which will clarify the strengths, weaknesses, and appropriate uses of each.

BIOSEM (Biomass Socio-economic Multiplier)

A model using socio-economic technique to capture the employment and income effects of bio-energy projects (ETSU 1998). The first step of the program is to examine the economic viability of feedstock production and conversion process. The financial analysis of the program is limited and offers to the investor only a basic appraisal approach.

RECAP (Renewable Energy Crop Analysis Program)

RECAP analyses all aspects of producing energy from energy crops (Moore 1996). It models all costs involved from energy crop production, harvesting, storage, transport and conversion. The model calculates cash flows and undertakes an investment appraisal by calculating NPV and IRR for both the farmer and the conversion plant operator.

BEAM (Bio-energy Assessment Model)

An Excel spreadsheet model for techno-economic assessment of a) biomass to electricity and b) biomass to ethanol schemes (Robertson 1998). BEAM covers particular types of feedstock, conversion technologies and energy products. It is a typical model for cost analysis. The user has only partial intervention facilities on input data.

BIOCOST (Bio-energy Crop Production Cost Model)

An Excel-based program that can be used to estimate the cost of producing hybrid poplar and switch-grass in seven regions of the United States (Walsh 1996). The model assumes default values for many parameters, such as combinations of machinery, establishment and cultivation techniques, planting densities, etc.

BEAVER (Biomass Economic Appraisal and eValuation ExpeRt)

An investment appraisal system for the economic evaluation of biomass cultivation (Agricultural University of Athens 1996). Its knowledge data bases currently hold detailed information about three biomass crops, namely sweet sorghum, poplar and willow. The model also uses genetic algorithms to identify optimal values for externally determined parameters.

MULTISEES

A multiple criteria decision making tool (GIS-based) for the analysis of integrated bio-energy systems in rural region in Southern Europe (Rozakis 2002). The model covers the integration of four different energy species (*Cynara cardunculus, Miscanthus,Robinia and*

Eucaliptus) and analyses four technologies of energy conversion (Fixed bed plus steam turbine, Fluidized bed plus steam turbine, Fluidized bed plus gas turbine and Combined heat and power). The model uses three different categories of default values (fuel parameters, technological parameters and economic parameters) that limit its flexibility.

ENERGY-10

ENERGY-10 software can identify the best combination of energy-efficient strategies, including daylighting, passive solar heating, and high-efficiency mechanical systems. Using ENERGY-10 at a project's start takes less than an hour and can result in energy savings of 40%-70%, with little or no increase in construction cost.

AGRICOST Model

The Laboratory of Agribusiness Management (Department of Agricultural Economics, Agricultural University of Athens) developed AGRICOST model, for cost analysis and investment appraisal of annual and/or perennial crop production, specializing on energy crops. The goal of the model is first to estimate the production cost of biomass at farm gate for different locations and secondly to examine the attractiveness of investing the farmer's land in biomass production. It can be used to analyze a single plantation or some combination of crops. Thus, it may analyze a farm with a number of different plantations, or various biomass crops grown in different farms, etc. The model comprises five different sections combined into one economic module.

1. *Input*: Supplies the data required for the analysis.
2. *Detail*: Data transformations and calculations of the necessary magnitudes for economic analysis. Basic cost analysis is performed in volume terms (i.e. man-hours, machine-hours, kilos, litres, etc.)
3. *Cost*: This section calculates cost details, by factor and by activity or operation (volumes × prices = values).
4. *Financial*: Estimates of future Profit and Loss Statements, Balance Sheets, and Cash Flows.
5. *Investment Appraisal*: Incorporates Investment Appraisal analysis and criteria useful for the determination of the attractiveness of the investment.

The required input consists of a number of small external databases and a few information tables that fully describe the biomass production process. Table *Crops* holds information about all cultivated crops, their average life and selling price. Another table, named *Harvesting Quantities* gives the user the opportunity to record volume of production that usually differs from year to year.

ECONPACK

A software package developed by USA Defense Department. ECONPACK is a unique economic analysis computer package available to engineers, economists, master planners, accountants, and other personnel throughout the Department of Defense and the Government (USA). It is a comprehensive program incorporating economic analysis calculations, documentation, and reporting capabilities. ECONPACK provides simple automated assistance in performing the necessary calculations and in producing certain specified report formats for EAs. It is structured so it can be used by non-economists to prepare complete, properly documented economic analyses.

The analytic capabilities of ECONPACK are generic, providing standardized economic analysis methodologies and calculations to evaluate a broad range of capital investment categories such as barracks, hospitals, family housing, information systems, utility plants, maintenance facilities, ranges, runways, commercially financed facilities, and equipment. It can also be used for the performance of sensitivity analyses, which are especially useful in situations involving substantial uncertainty about future costs.

FEAM

The Functional Economic Analysis Model (FEAM) is intended to support analyses of potential cost-saving alternatives for Department of Defense information management, and to aid functional managers in presenting their business case. The model is designed to allow the user to enter costs and receive information for a series of alternatives to a cost baseline. The baseline represents expected costs for a given function using existing processes to satisfy projected workload. The model takes the user-supplied information and performs a risk-adjusted, discounted cash flow analysis for each alternative. The results are presented in a series of graphs and tables.

LCPSIM (Least-Cost Planning SIMulation model)

It is developed by California Department of Water Resources (Ray Hoagland, Division of Planning and Local Assistance). The model has been applied to the San Francisco Bay and South Coast hydrologic regions at the 2020 level of demand to determine the regional economic benefit value of additional State Water Project deliveries. Main Features and Capabilities of the model are:

- *Data-driven* in order to represent different water service systems without changing the model code.
- Spatial scale at *hydrologic region/planning area.*
- Simulation runs through a hydrologic sequence of supplies and rainfall-correlated demands at a specified level of future demand (e.g., 2030) on a *yearly* time step.
- *Reliability enhancement options* are adopted based cost minimization ($ per thousand acre-feet) and include long-run demand reduction and supply augmentation measures, such as toilet retrofit and wastewater recycling, to reduce frequency, magnitude, and duration of shortage events.
- The effect of conservation options on water treatment and distribution costs and on regional reuse and, consequently, on the value of supply based on whether the options affect interior or exterior use is taken into account.
- Cost of *reliability enhancement* (thousands of $) expressed as a function of the level of adoption of *reliability enhancement options* (thousands of acre-feet).
- *Shortage contingency measures* such as water transfers (based on single-year least cost optimization and transfer costs by source and year type) and shortage allocation by *water use category* in the region/planning area (residential, commercial, industrial, and large landscaping) are used for shortage management.

- *Expected economic losses* (thousands of $) are produced by an *economic loss function* which uses the percentage size of shortage (foregone use) events generated by the simulation as well as the percentage size of each *water use category*.
- *Demand hardening* is computed as a function of the level of use of demand reduction measures and used to adjust *expected economic losses*.
- Cost of *unreliability* (thousands of $) is expressed as a function of the level of adoption of *reliability enhancement options* (thousands of acre-feet) and includes *expected economic losses* as well as the expected costs of *shortage contingency measures*.
- *Reliability management cost* (thousands of $) includes the cost of *reliability enhancement*, the cost of *unreliability*, and the cost of carryover storage operations, conveyance, potable and wastewater treatment, and distribution.
- The *least-cost reliability management plan* is identified by minimizing *reliability management cost* expressed as a function of the level of *reliability enhancement*.
- Operations of *carryover storage facilities* available to the region/planning area (including ground water banking and associated put and take rules) are used for reliability management in LCPSIM.

COSTAB

COSTAB is the project costing component of a software series to improve efficiency and effectiveness of Project Processing activities (The International AIDS Economics Network (IAEN), http://www.iaen.org/models.html).

COSTAB 32, upgraded in 2001 and 2008 by ADB, is a 32-bit version of the software designed to operate under various operating systems (Windows 95, Windows 98, Windows ME, Windows 2000 and Windows XP.

Features of COSTAB 32:

- helps mission leaders, project economists, and financial analysts to organize and analyze project costing data in the course of project preparation and appraisal
- calculates physical and price contingencies, taxes and foreign exchange
- displays data in detailed cost tables
- coverts financial costs to economic costs for use in economic analysis

8.3. Softwares /Tools for Financial Analysis

Various commercial software packages are available for economic analysis, project evaluation, tax, depreciation calculation, etc. You can develop your required tool in Excel for calculating various aspects of financial analysis.

In addition, in-built facilities of Excel can be used to calculate various components of financial analysis (such as PV, FV, NPV, IRR, etc.). Short notes on some existing software packages are given below.

mmSensitivity 2.07

mmSensitivity (Michail A. Morozov, 2002) is a sensitivity analysis add-in for Microsoft Excel 97, 98, 2000, and 2001 for Windows. This tool allows to perform a correct sensitivity analysis, thin adjustment of models parameters, and to assist in solving of scientific and technical, engineering, economic problems connected to forecasting of target parameters, dependent from several data-ins, which amount is not limited. Newest version of this product can be obtained from http://mm-soft.narod.ru/.

ECONPACK

ECONOPACK for Windows—an economic analysis tool developed by the U.S. Army Corps of Engineers in support of DOD funding requests, which is described in earlier section.

Investment Valuation Model
This model is compatible with Excel 97 or above.

Whitestone **CostLab**
It is a cost analysis tool.
Source URL: https://secure.whitestoneresearch.com/products/view/CostLab-Level-5#costlabVideo

eVALUator

eVALUator is an easy-to-use Windows-based program that calculates the lifecycle benefits of investments that improve building design. It analyzes the financial benefits from buildings that reduce energy cost, raise employee productivity, and enhance tenant satisfaction. It also provides building owners, developers, tenants, architects, engineers, and facility managers with the financial information necessary to make sound decisions about building improvements. An eVALUator financial analysis considers the following factors over the life of a project:

- Financing costs
- Tax implications
- Energy costs
- Replacement costs and intervals
- Operation and maintenance costs
- Opportunity costs for money (discount rates)
- The impact of inflation
- Non-energy benefits (such as improved occupant productivity and tenant retention)

eVALUator produces a set of "bottom-line" economic parameters as well as a year-by-year cash flow analysis. This includes:

- Net present value of lifecycle costs and savings
- Savings-to-investment ratio
- Adjusted internal rate of return

Source URL: http://www.energydesignresources.com/resource/131/

Exercise

1) What do you mean by a "Model"?
2) Discuss types and functions of models.
3) What are the (a) objectives, and (b) purposes of economic and financial model?
4) What are the types of scenario analysis conducted with economic model?
5) Write short on:
   (a) Model validation and verification
   (b) Delphi analysis
6) Write down the fields of application of economic model.
7) Write short note on o6 (six) economic models.
8) Name some softwares/tools for financial analysis.
9) Perform PV, FV, NPV, and IRR calculation using Excel spreadsheet with sample data.

References

Agricultural University of Athens (1996). "Models for the Economic Evaluation of Biomass Production as an Alternative Land Use in the European Community", *Final Report, Project No:AIR3-CT93-0985.*

ETSU (1998). BIOSEM: A socio-economic technique to capture the employment and income effects of bioenergy projects. *Manual6.doc, Version 2.0,* ETSU.

Michail A. Morozov (2002). mmSensitivity 2.07. http://mm-soft.narod.ru/.

Moore, A. and K. Dury (1996). "RECAP Service Center, 1996". *Proceedings of the 9th European Bioenergy Conference: Biomass for energy and environment. Oxford: Pergamon,* 1996. Pp 1955-60.

Robertson, K. A. and J. B. Ford-Robertson (1998). "Final Report for Task XIII Integrated Bioenergy Systems", March 1998. *IEA Report.*

Rozakis, S., Soldatos, P. G., Kalivroussis, L. and I. Nicolaou (2002). "Multiple Criteria Decision- Making on Bio-Energy Projects: Evaluation of Bio-Electricity in Farsala Plain, Greece", *Journal of Geographic Information and Decision Analysis* 5(1): 49 64.

Walsh, M. E. and D. Becker (1996). "BIOCOST: A Software Program to Estimate the Cost of Producing Bioenergy Crops", *Proceedings, BIOENERGY '96 - The Seventh National Bioenergy Conference: Partnerships to Develop and Apply Biomass Technologies,* September 1996. Nashville, Tennessee. pp. 15-20.

INDEX

A

annual exceedance probability (AEP), 149, 150
annualized value, 60, 66, 106, 117, 121, 128, 134
annuity, 96, 106
average cost, 13, 22, 81, 106, 166
average recurrence interval (ARI), 149, 150, 156

B

benefit-cost ratio, 2, 32
break-even analysis, 26, 27, 28
break-even point, 25, 26, 28
budgeting, viii, 27, 34, 103, 143
buyer, 11

C

calibration process, 176
candidates for sensitivity analysis, 145
capital recovery, 167, 169
cash flow, 39, 40, 99, 100, 102, 103, 104, 105, 106, 107, 109, 114, 122, 124, 127, 141, 177, 182
cash flow margin, 40
challenger, 165
competitive risks, 146
compound factor, 105, 111
compounding, 103, 110, 111, 113, 114, 119, 121, 122
contingency, viii, 82, 87, 93, 96, 143, 146, 179, 180
cost analyses, viii, 29
cost curve, 14, 25, 64, 167, 168
cost depletion, 50
cost effectiveness, 2, 30, 86, 101, 121
cost estimation, 16, 20, 76, 80, 81, 83, 96
cost function, 14, 79, 80, 94, 165, 166

cost index, 21, 80, 94
cost of capital, 10, 126, 127, 136, 137, 141
cost-benefit analysis, 29, 31, 32
cost-capacity relation, 81
cost-effectiveness, 29, 30, 101

D

data, iv, vii, viii, 3, 4, 17, 19, 27, 58, 62, 69, 70, 74, 75, 76, 78, 79, 80, 81, 84, 89, 92, 93, 95, 96, 97, 117, 140, 143, 144, 145, 152, 161, 162, 166, 167, 174, 177, 178, 180, 181, 182
data checking, 95
decision rules, vii, viii
declining- balance, 47
defender, 165
deflation, 20, 42, 43, 44, 51, 64, 102, 146
delaying the replacement, 168
demand, 4, 5, 6, 10, 11, 12, 13, 21, 41, 43, 44, 64, 70, 71, 72, 73, 74, 90, 92, 95, 96, 97, 100, 153, 158, 168, 174, 179, 180
demand curve, 10, 11, 12, 13, 64, 174
depletion, 49, 50, 54, 55, 65, 106
depreciation, 32, 36, 38, 44, 45, 46, 47, 48, 49, 53, 64, 65, 160, 162, 163, 166, 168, 169, 180
depreciation accounting method, 47
design capacity estimation, 95
diminishing marginal productivity, 22
direct cost, 17, 20, 52, 53, 77, 85, 86, 93, 96, 169
direct indicator, 124
discount factor, 103, 107, 111
discount rate, 101, 103, 104, 105, 106, 107, 108, 109, 110, 114, 116, 121, 122, 123, 124, 129, 130, 131, 133, 135, 137, 139, 142, 144, 145, 148, 181
discounted cash flow (DCF), 103, 104, 143, 179
discounting, 32, 105, 107, 108, 109, 110, 111, 113, 121, 123

discounting of costs, 32

E

economic analysis, vii, viii, 1, 2, 5, 6, 8, 69, 73, 76,
    95, 99, 143, 145, 175, 178, 179, 180, 181
economic criterion, 3, 5, 8
economic growth rate, 51, 64
economic life, 46, 61, 67, 106, 117, 128, 158, 166
economic model, 174, 175, 177, 182
economic principles, vii, 1
economic service life, 46, 167
economic service life', 46
economic viability, viii, 3, 99, 123, 135, 177
economics, iv, viii, 3, 9, 10, 12, 13, 22, 30, 31, 176
economists, 10, 31, 33, 103, 174, 177, 178, 180
economy, iv, viii, ix, 1, 9, 11, 13, 25, 41, 42, 43, 44,
    50, 51, 64, 99, 123, 157, 174, 175
effective service life, 46, 106
endogenous variable, 174
engineering, iv, vii, viii, 2, 3, 4, 5, 6, 8, 9, 15, 18, 20,
    21, 30, 46, 47, 52, 62, 64, 65, 67, 69, 70, 75, 76,
    81, 83, 90, 97, 99, 121, 143, 144, 151, 155, 157,
    181
engineering economics, 5, 15
equilibrium point, 13
equipment replacement, ix, 160, 165, 167, 170
errors in replacement, 170
exceedance probability, 149
exogenous variable, 174
expert opinion approach, 78

F

finance, 10, 21, 70, 103, 151
financial analysis, vii, viii, 5, 17, 99, 107, 121, 138,
    141, 142, 145, 175, 177, 180, 181, 182
financial risk, 146
fixed costs, 14, 16, 27, 28, 29, 38, 39
free cash flow, 40
full budget, 35
future value, 43, 100, 103, 104, 105, 110, 111, 112,
    113, 114, 116

G

GDP, 50, 51, 52, 64
gross domestic product, 1, 51
gross national product (GNP), 50, 51, 64
gross profit, 36, 37, 38
gross profit margin, 37, 38

I

incremental cost, 17
indicators, viii, 3, 4, 31, 74, 123, 140, 141
indirect cost, 17, 20, 52, 53, 77, 82, 86, 87, 96, 169
inflation, viii, 1, 9, 20, 32, 43, 44, 51, 55, 56, 64, 66,
    80, 94, 95, 101, 102, 108, 146, 181
initial cost or first cost, 17
initial investment, 3, 101, 107, 110, 165, 167
interest, 1, 10, 17, 38, 42, 43, 48, 101, 102, 103, 104,
    106, 108, 113, 114, 116, 117, 118, 120, 121, 122,
    124, 126, 128, 134, 146, 160, 161, 162, 163, 164,
    166, 169, 171, 173, 174
internal rate of return, 103, 109, 123, 124, 182
irreducible factors, 164

J

junk cost, 17

L

least-cost option, 99
locational effect, 21, 40, 94

M

margin analysis, 36
marginal cost, 22, 23, 24, 52, 65
marginal product, 22, 24
marginal revenue, 23, 24
marginal revenue product, 24
marginal utility, 13
minimum attractive rate of return (MARR), 127,
    136, 137, 138, 139, 141
modeling process, 173
models, ix, 79, 141, 150, 153, 166, 167, 173, 174,
    176, 177, 180, 181, 182
mutually exclusive project, 124, 125
mutually independent project, 125

N

net benefit, 2, 3, 24, 25, 108, 109, 113, 133, 134
net financial benefit, 5, 25
net future value (NFV), 105, 121
net present value (NPV), vi, viii, 37, 103, 105, 106,
    107, 108, 109, 110, 114, 115, 116, 121, 122, 123,
    124, 125, 129, 130, 131, 132, 133, 136, 137, 138,
    139, 145, 177, 180, 182

nominal and real value, 121

O

operating costs, 161, 162, 163, 164, 167, 169, 170, 171
operating income, 38
operating margin, 38, 39
operation risk, 147
opportunity cost, 17, 20, 33, 34, 52, 53, 58, 66, 108, 123, 161

P

parametric approach, 78
partial budget, 2, 29, 34, 35
policy analysis, ix, 175, 176
political risks, 146
population growth, 71, 95
present value, 37, 43, 52, 100, 103, 104, 105, 106, 109, 110, 111, 113, 114, 116, 117, 123, 128, 135, 136, 167, 171, 175, 182
price, 10, 11, 12, 13, 15, 18, 19, 20, 21, 24, 26, 27, 28, 29, 31, 33, 35, 36, 40, 41, 42, 44, 46, 47, 51, 52, 55, 58, 59, 62, 66, 67, 75, 77, 78, 79, 80, 82, 84, 85, 87, 91, 93, 94, 97, 115, 116, 134, 153, 155, 159, 164, 174, 178, 180
price level, 12, 26, 41, 51
probability of exceedence, 71
probability of occurrence, 145, 147, 148
profit margins, ix, 36, 43, 157
profitability, vii, 2, 13, 26, 27, 33, 34, 35, 36, 39, 76
profitability analysis, 2
project, vii, viii, 2, 3, 4, 5, 6, 7, 8, 9, 16, 17, 19, 20, 27, 29, 31, 32, 36, 37, 52, 53, 58, 63, 64, 65, 66, 68, 69, 70, 71, 72, 73, 75, 76, 77, 78, 79, 80, 81, 82, 83, 85, 86, 87, 88, 92, 93, 94, 95, 96, 97, 99, 100, 101, 102, 103, 104, 106, 107, 108, 109, 111, 114, 115, 116, 117, 122, 123, 124, 125, 126, 127, 129, 130, 131, 132, 133, 134, 135, 136, 137, 138, 139, 140, 141, 142, 143, 144, 145, 146, 147, 148, 151, 153, 154, 155, 175, 178, 180, 181
project judgment, 140
project selection, 29

R

ranking of alternatives, 145
real value, 101
recurring cost, 18
replacement decisions, 165, 167

replacement models, 170
replacement timing, ix, 157
residual value, 46
return on investment, 39
return period, 151
revenue curve, 14, 15, 25, 27, 64
revenue function, 14, 27, 64
revenues, 27, 39, 103, 110, 161, 162
risk management, 148, 151
risks, viii, 132, 143, 145, 146, 147, 148, 151, 152, 155
running cost, 17, 60, 66, 171

S

safe investment, 126, 127
safe return rate, 127, 136, 137, 141
salvage value, 44, 46, 47, 48, 49, 53, 63, 65, 68, 102, 114, 121, 128, 134, 142, 159, 160, 161, 162, 163, 165, 166, 167
seasonality, 21, 40
selection criteria, 8, 125
sensitivity analyses, 145, 179
simple interest, 117
single installment, 118
softwares, 177, 182
stages of cost estimation, 96
straight line method, 48, 49
sum of-the-digits method, 47
suppler, 11
supply, 3, 4, 5, 10, 11, 12, 13, 21, 41, 43, 44, 47, 58, 59, 64, 66, 72, 73, 95, 100, 126, 158, 174, 179
supply curve, 10, 11, 12, 64
system, iv, ix, 1, 13, 18, 19, 24, 29, 34, 35, 46, 47, 58, 59, 63, 64, 66, 68, 70, 79, 83, 101, 123, 144, 153, 157, 158, 159, 169, 173, 175, 176, 177

T

tax, 1, 16, 18, 44, 45, 46, 47, 56, 57, 64, 78, 79, 80, 83, 84, 85, 146, 174, 180
tax depreciation, 44, 64
taxable income, 45, 56, 57
technology, 1, 2, 3, 6, 7, 8, 34, 106, 158, 175
the quantity supplied, 10, 12
total cost, 4, 16, 20, 21, 23, 25, 27, 30, 31, 32, 33, 35, 36, 52, 53, 57, 58, 59, 61, 62, 63, 64, 65, 68, 79, 82, 91, 93, 94, 97, 108, 114, 115, 124, 135, 160, 161, 162
total net profit, 36
turnover ratio, 82, 91, 97
types of data, 70, 75, 95

U

uncertainties, viii, 77, 143, 144, 145, 146, 147, 151, 152, 153, 155
uniform annual cash-flow, 104, 110

V

validation, 176, 182
variable costs, 14, 17, 26, 29, 38, 60
verification, iv, 182